The United Kingdom
Mathematics Trust

Title: Plane Euclidean Geometry: Theory and Problems

Authors: Christopher Bradley and Tony Gardiner

Editor: Geoff Smith

ISBN 0 9536823 6 6

Published by:
The United Kingdom Mathematics Trust (UKMT), an educational charity. This organization can be contacted via:

Maths Challenges Office,
School of Mathematics,
University of Leeds,
Leeds LS2 9JT (+44 113 343 2339)

e-mail: publishing@ukmt.org.uk

URL: http://www.ukmt.org.uk

Editorial board: Christopher Bradley, Nick Lord and Geoff Smith

Printed in the United Kingdom by Cromwell Press Trowbridge

Contents

Introduction

Euclidean geometry is perhaps *the* richest source of challenging problems for the young mathematician. This book seeks to make this subject accessible to a larger group by cultivating *geometrical thinking*. Given the current state of geometrical instruction, it has been necessary to provide an outline of the *theory* of Euclidean Geometry starting more or less from scratch. We have not tried to produce a comprehensive account of the development of the subject; instead we have sought to devise a guide to help able students master the relevant techniques for themselves *by solving problems*, with the minimum amount of help. This help comes in three forms.

The question of what one can take for granted when solving a geometry problem has always been a source of some confusion. The first kind of help these notes provides stems from the simple, step by step development of the subject, which should help students see more clearly *what may be assumed to be known* when tackling each set of problems.

The second kind of support we have provided is that we have tried to make the text illustrative of a wide variety of useful methods and techniques, and to ensure that it contains all the main theorems and formulae the student is likely to encounter. However, not all the theorems are fully proved in the text: some are left with gaps for you to fill in. Though the text contains all the results which are needed to solve the problems in the Exercises, some of the problems contain additional important material which you should incorporate in your geometrical "armoury of knowledge".

Finally, direct help is given with the Exercises by providing hints to the starred problems in Chapters 1 and 2 and hints or solutions to all Exercises in Chapters 3–7. **These hints should not be used until a serious effort has been made to solve the problem first.**

At some stage or other we have solved each of the problems, but that is no guarantee that everything is correct! We apologise for any remaining errors. On behalf of subsequent users of these notes, we ask *all users* to tell us if they find any errors or misprints.

Altogether there are seven chapters. They are meant to be read in order. However, if the contents of a particular chapter are familiar, and if you have tackled similar problems before, you can probably skip ahead to the next chapter without missing much.

Chapter 1 is essentially introductory, and is mainly concerned with putting the subject on a firm logical foundation. In general this follows the development of Euclid, though it does not stick to his flawed axioms. The approach chosen seeks to minimise the formality of the initial framework; this is, after all, a treatment intended for beginners and not for pure mathematicians. Thus, for example, no formal attempt is made to grapple with notions of "betweenness". Those who have sympathy with these self-imposed constraints will find that the approach allows students to gain some insight into the *structure* of Euclidean geometry and to get down to solving interesting problems without being unduly diverted by the minutiae of a complete axiom system. Having laid the foundations, we then go through the basic theorems on congruence as far as areas and Pythagoras's theorem.

Chapter 2 introduces the idea of similarity. It then explores the consequences of congruence and similarity. There is also a brief review of trigonometrical formulae. All this is then applied to prove the basic properties of triangles and polygons.

Chapter 3 reviews the basic properties of the circle, including the concept of similitude.

In Chapter 4 the more advanced properties of the triangle and its circles are studied, using purely geometrical and trigonometric methods.

Chapter 5 reviews much of this work once more in the context of vectors and areal, or barycentric, co-ordinates. Readers should reflect on the relationship between the methods of Chapters 4 and 5. However, the relative merits of the two approaches cannot always be resolved objectively: the decision as to which method to use in any given problem will depend partly on your own personal preferences.

Chapter 6 provides guidance on how to tackle geometrical inequalities - a subject which is still developing, and which is something of a favourite with Olympiad problem setters.

In Chapter 7, which completes our survey, we admit (for the first time!) the existence of Cartesian co-ordinates and complex numbers, and identify certain types of problem for which related techniques are likely to be successful. Inversion also appears here for the first time: though a very beautiful topic, its application to solving Olympiad problems must be regarded as a sophisticated sideline rather than a mainstream necessity.

Editorial comments

We hope that *Plane Euclidean Geometry: Theory and Problems* will be the first of many texts published by the United Kingdom Mathematics Trust. We will try to publish books at low price but of high quality, so that students in the United Kingdom and the rest of the world will have access to excellent materials.

Geoff Smith, Bath April 2005

Chapter 1

Axioms, Congruence, Area and Pythagoras

---

[1]This abbreviation means *flourished*, and is used when exact birth or death dates are unknown

9

1.1 From Descartes (1596-1650 AD) to Euclid (fl. 300 BC)

Nowadays geometry is often presented as a *pot pourri* which entirely neglects the logical thread that can make the subject consistent and satisfying. Not surprisingly, many intelligent pupils develop a distaste for "pure" geometry, and show their preference by using co-ordinate methods whenever possible.

Now co-ordinate geometry is a powerful way of solving certain sorts of geometry problems. Unfortunately it disguises the elegant and instructive logical structure of geometry by smothering everything with real *numbers*, whose logical structure is simply taken for granted.

If we take real numbers for granted, then we can define *points* to correspond to ordered pairs (x, y) of real numbers, and can define *lines* to correspond to equations of the form $ax + by + c = 0$. If we then assume Pythagoras's theorem as "known", we can define *circles* to correspond to equations of the form $(x-a)^2 + (y-b)^2 = r^2$.

Though this is a powerful method, it is not without its own logical difficulties (What exactly is a real number ?). But the most significant weakness of a co-ordinate approach is that it presents a biased view of every geometrical problem by imposing an arbitrary co-ordinate system which may well be inappropriate for the problem in hand. Thus, while we can all sketch the curve $y = 1/x$, we may find it much harder to recognise that $3x^2 - 3y^2 + 2\sqrt{3}xy = 3$ represents the same curve with respect to differently chosen co-ordinate axes!

Those who go far enough in co-ordinate geometry are bound to notice that the further one goes, the more complicated it becomes. Indeed the use of a co-ordinate approach to many of the problems from more advanced geometry, particularly those with complicated figures, all too often leads to algebra which is almost too horrible to contemplate. One reason for this is that co-ordinate geometry takes each problem back to first principles - the equations of lines, circles, etc. so that the elementary theorems required to prove a new result have to be re-established on the way to a solution. Another reason, as we have seen, is that elegance in co-ordinate geometry often depends on choosing an appropriate co-ordinate system, and it may only become clear which co-ordinate system is "appropriate" *after* you have solved the problem.

Co-ordinate geometry has its moments (for example, in connection with conic sections). When it works, it has the advantage of requiring less insight than other methods, so that more human beings can appreciate and use it. That is one reason why so many students try to use it. It also explains why those who set Olympiad problems – problems which are intended to provide a serious challenge for a relatively small number of talented students go to great lengths to devise problems which cannot be easily solved using co-ordinate methods.

In general, given an Olympiad problem involving an assembly of lines and circles, a *purely* geometrical approach - that is, a *non-co-ordinate* method, will not just be "better" but may be the only reasonable way of proceeding

1.2 From Euclid (fl. 300 BC) to Hilbert (1862-1943 AD)

Building up Euclidean plane geometry in a logically correct way *without using co-ordinates* is a delicate task. To make the logical structure clear one would like to base this geometry on a small number of simple ideas - such as the notions of *point, line* and *circle*, together with the related notions of *angle, length* and *area*.

What then is a *point*? In one sense we all know what we mean by a "point" . But if we are forced to explain (without using co-ordinates!), we will have to admit that it is rather hard to express our ideas convincingly. Whatever we mean, it is certainly more abstract than "the smallest physical pencil mark", as Euclid and his contemporaries realised.

"A *point*," wrote Euclid, is "that which has no part." It would be hard to disagree that this curious expression does indeed capture one particular property of what we imagine as a point, though it is hard to see how one could ever *use* such a definiton in practice. Moreover, this cannot possibly *define* exactly what we mean, since, for example, the same would be equally true of the empty set.

Fortunately we need not enter into philosophical debate about what a "point" is and what it is not. Mathematicians discovered early in the last century that one can never hope to *define* such basic objects from first principles. One reason for this is that, to make sense, every definition of a *new* kind of object has to be expressed in terms of other objects and relationships which are *already assumed to be known.*

Thus mathematicians had to accept that what matters is **not** what a "point" or "line" really is, but *how they behave*. Thus the notions "point" and "line" have to remain *undefined terms* within our geometry.

David Hilbert (1862-1943), who produced the first logically sound approach to Euclidean geometry in 1899, summed up this idea that one can never define the basic objects in a theory by saying,
"Whenever I say "point", "line", or "plane", one must be able to say instead "table", "chair", or "beer mug"."
(He was actually standing on a railway platform and not sitting in a pub at the time he said this!).

Thus what should really concern us is not the meaning of the fundamental entities "point" and "line", but the rules they have to satisfy. The modern name for these rules is *axioms* , and this is the term we shall use.

Strictly speaking these axioms tell us exactly what we are allowed to assume about the *undefined* terms "point" and "line". It is nevertheless helpful to have a mental image of the properties that these axioms are trying to capture. Thus it is useful to imagine a "point" as an "infinitely small dot", and a "line" as an "infinitely thin straight line extending to infinity in both directions". Whenever we write "line" we mean "*straight* line extending to infinity in both directions." These images are however aids to understanding: they are not part of the formal logical structure of the geometry. Any diagrams which we may draw on the basis of these images will be correct only insofar as they *reflect the properties* of truly geometrical *points* and *lines* which are stated in the axioms of our geometry.

So let us imagine that we have two sorts of things called *points* (usually denoted by capital letters $A, B, C, \ldots, P, Q, \ldots$) and *lines* (usually denoted by lower case italic letters such as $l, m, n, \ldots$). We now have to specify the basic rules, or *axioms* which these entities have to satisfy.

Axiom 1 It is possible to draw exactly one line through any two points.

If the two points are called P and Q, then the line will some-
times be denoted by $\overleftrightarrow{PQ}$. This first axiom explicitly requires that
through any two points there will be one and only one line. Thus,
provided P and Q are distinct points, $\overleftrightarrow{PQ}$ will denote the one and
only line through them both. In particular, two *distinct* lines either
meet in *exactly* one common point, or *do not meet at all*.

If we were trying to capture the essence of 3-dimensional geometry, we would have to allow for the fact that in 3-dimensions, two
lines which do not meet at all may *not* be parallel, for they may
be *skew* lines (like the opposite edges of a regular tetrahedron).
However, since we are concerned here solely with *plane* geometry,
it is reasonable to introduce the following definition.

Definition Two lines which do not meet at all will be said to be
parallel.

This definition is appropriate only because a later axiom (*Axiom 3*) will force our geometry to be *plane* or *2-dimensional* geometry.

While *Axiom 1* guarantees the existence of just one infinite line
$\overleftrightarrow{PQ}$ through any two given points P, Q, most geometry problems
are concerned *not* with the whole line $\overleftrightarrow{PQ}$ but with line *segments*.

Definition Given two points P, Q, that portion of the line through
P and Q which lies between P and Q is called the *line segment PQ*.

In Euclidean geometry there is no *fixed* way of measuring length.
But we can always *introduce* a unit of length by *choosing* two *distinct* points P and Q, and declaring the line segment PQ to be
our basic *unit of length*. Given any other two points A and B it

is possible then to prove that there is a precise way of identifying "how many times" the basic unit segment PQ will fit into the line segment AB, and this then determines the *length* of the line segment AB *in terms of our chosen unit*.

More precisely, what we can determine is the *ratio of the two segments AB and PQ*. However, if AB happens to be the diagonal of a square and PQ is one of the sides of the square, then this ratio is *irrational*. In such a case the question of "how many times PQ will fit into AB" involves subtleties which we shall not enter into. We shall thus take for granted that there is a procedure which allows us to refer unambiguously to the ratio $AB : PQ$ of any two given line segments AB and PQ (provided $P \neq Q$), and hence to calculate the *length* of AB in terms of any chosen unit PQ.

The most important thing to note at this stage is that the value of the ratio of two given line segments has to be determined *by logical reasoning*: **there is no place in Euclidean geometry for approximate measuring!** (For example, the ratio of the diagonal to the side of a square is $\sqrt{2}$, and definitely not 1.414 or any other approximation.)

We shall often use the notation AB to denote not only the line segment, but also the *length* of that line segment measured in terms of some (unspecified) unit.

Thus, if A, B, C are three points on a line, the "equation"

$$AB + BC = AC$$

may then be interpreted in two ways as indicating either

1. that the two *lengths* on the LHS add to the *length* on the RHS, or

2. that the two *segments* on the LHS fit together to make up the *segment* on the RHS

If B lies between A and C, then this should cause no problems. But if C lies between A and B, the equation makes sense only if we introduce some convention about *signed lengths* and *directed segments*, with the segment BA having the *opposite direction* to AB. Then, if C lies between A and B, the *directed* segment BC in the above equation has the *opposite direction* to the *directed* segment AB, and so can be assigned a length with the *opposite sign*, so the equation still makes sense. This can, of course, only be done sensibly if the three points A, B, C all lie on one line.

In the same spirit, once we have clarified what we mean by **angle** $\angle AOB$, and by the *size* of such an angle, comparisons of angles have to be based on *reasoning; there is no place in Euclidean geometry for protractors, estimates or other approximate methods*. As for segments and lengths, we will usually denote the $\angle AOB$ and the size of the angle $\angle AOB$ in exactly the same way as "$\angle AOB$". If AO, BO and CO are line segments with a common endpoint O, we can thus write "equations" like

$$\angle AOB + \angle BOC = \angle AOC.$$

If the segment BO lies "between" the segments AO and CO, the meaning should be clear. But if segment CO lies "between" the segments AO and BO, then the equation will only make sense if we interpret the angles as *signed* angles.

In general we take $\angle POQ$ to be *positive* if the rotation of the line segment from OP to OQ is *anticlockwise*.

We may therefore, if we wish, *choose* a basic unit of length and assign to each line segment PQ a *length* which is a real number ≥ 0.

In contrast the unit of angle measurement is in some sense *fixed*, in that there is something rather special about a *complete turn*. Since it is rather difficult to think about a complete turn as a *bona fide angle*, we express this *universal* property of angle measurement in terms of *straight angles* (that is, of angles like $\angle ABC$ where A, B, C all lie in order on one straight line).

Axiom 2 All straight angles are equal to one another.

Definition Any angle which is exactly half a straight angle is called a *right angle.*

Since all straight angles are equal to one another, we have as a consequence:

Consequence 1 All right angles are equal to one another.

Consequence 2 Let A, B, C be three points in order on the line l, and let D, B, E be three points in order on the line m (so l and m cross at the point B). If $\angle ABD = \angle DBC$, then $\angle ABD = \angle DBC = \angle CBE = \angle EBA$ so all four angles are right angles.

Proof
$\angle ABD$ and $\angle DBC$ are both exactly half a straight angle, and $\angle DBC + \angle CBE = \angle DBE$ is a straight angle, so $\angle CBE$ is exactly half a straight angle.
Similarly $\angle CBE + \angle EBA = \angle CBA$ is a straight angle, so $\angle EBA$ is exactly half a straight angle. Hence all four angles are right angles. ∎

This result means that there can be no ambiguity in saying that two lines "meet at right angles".

Definition Two lines m, n which meet at right angles are called *perpendicular.*

Whenever it is convenient to do so we shall refer to angles by their sizes *in degrees*; that is, with every right angle being equal to 90°.

The next axiom is more important than it may seem at first sight: its full significance will only become apparent later. At this stage we merely observe that it is clearly more complicated than the other axioms.

For many centuries mathematicians struggled to find some way of showing that this axiom was unnecessary - that is, it could be *proved* to be a logical consequence of the other axioms. Then, around 1830, three mathematicians in three different countries – Gauss (Northern Germany), Bolyai (Hungary), and Lobachewsky (Russia) – came to the conclusion more or less simultaneously that *non-Euclidean* geometries (in which this axiom does not hold) were perfectly consistent!

Axiom 3 (Parallel axiom) If a straight line cuts two straight lines m, n so that the interior angles on one side add up to less than a straight angle, then the two lines m, n meet on that side.

Thus, if in the diagram, $x + y < 180°$ the lines m, n will meet on the left.

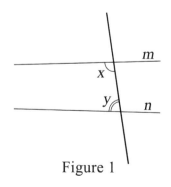

Figure 1

Be warned: *Axiom 3* is more subtle than it looks. For example, it does **not** say "if m and n meet on the left, then $x + y < 180°$," though it is logically equivalent to the statement that

"if m and n do **not** meet on the left, then $x + y \geq 180°$".

1.3 Ruler and compass constructions

Euclid's approach to geometry is strongly influenced by the idea of geometrical *construction*. Indeed, the geometry of the Ancient Greeks may be best understood as an attempt to pinpoint what can, and what cannot, be *constructed rigorously* using just a *straightedge* and a *pair of compasses*.

From such a viewpoint, *Axiom 1* is then the key assertion that

whenever we have succeeded in constructing two points P and Q, we can always **construct** *the line through them and that there is just one such line. This explains what is meant by a "straightedge" in Euclidean constructions: that is, "a straightedge is an infinite ruler with no markings on it".*

Thus a straightedge can be used to "construct" or "draw" the (infinite) straight line through two points, provided these points have already been constructed.

From our modern viewpoint however, the important part of *Axiom 1* is not that the line through two given points *exists*, or can be *constructed*. For us, the crucial part of *Axiom 1* is that this line is *unique*. The same problem simply does not arise with circles.

Definition Given two points P and Q, the *circle* through Q with *centre* P is the set of all points X such that $PX = PQ$. The length, or segment, PQ is called the *radius* of the circle.

To us, this is a perfectly satisfactory definition which allows us to talk sensibly about "*the* circle which has centre at the point P and which passes through the point Q". Euclid however gave this definition the status of an axiom, because he wanted to stress the basic idea that "given P and Q, it is always possible to *construct* the circle through Q with centre P". There is a whole theory of which geometrical *constructions* can, and which cannot, be carried out using "ruler (without marks) and compasses". The related problems provide excellent material to help students build up chains of permissible deductions. By way of introduction we consider here just one such problem.

Problem Given three distinct points A, B, C is it possible to construct the circle with centre A and radius equal to BC?

This problem can be rephrased:

"Can we find some way of constructing a segment AX (*with one endpoint* at the given point A) which is equal to the given segment BC?"

Work through (that is, think through logically and *carry out physically*) the following construction and see how it achieves this goal. Make sure you can justify each step.

Construction
Step 1 Draw the circle centre A, radius AB.
Step 2 Draw the circle centre B, radius BA.
Step 3 If we call one of the points of intersection of these two circles F, then the triangle FAB is equilateral ($FA = AB = BF$).
Step 4 Draw the circle centre B, radius BC. Extend the segment FB to meet this circle at G.
Step 5 Draw the circle centre F, radius FG. Extend the segment FA to meet this circle at H.
Step 6 Then $AH = BG = BC$, so we are finished.

If in addition to the original requirement, we want the segment AX

to lie along a particluar line m through the point A, we need an additional step:

Step 7 Draw the circle centre A, radius AH, and let X be the relevant point where this circle meets the line m.

Note The above construction may be interpreted in the language of transformations as the composition of three *rotations*

$$BC \rightarrow BG, FBG \rightarrow FAH, AH \rightarrow AX.$$

The construction on the line m of a line segment AX equal to a given line segment BC raises two questions, one about segments and a related question about angles.

Suppose that Mr X and Mrs Y use different methods to construct points X and Y on the segment AZ, where AX and AY are both equal to BC .

Question
Can we be sure that $X = Y$?
Clearly, if $AX = AY (= BC)$, then XY would have to have length zero. Thus this question could be rephrased: suppose that a segment XY has length zero. Can we conclude that $X = Y$?

Strictly speaking, we should answer *"No. We **cannot** prove **logically** that $X = Y$ on the basis of our axioms"*. However, the additional axioms which should strictly be included are likely to confuse rather than to help the beginner. We shall therefore content ourselves with the following:

Axiom 4(a) If X, Y **lie on the segment** AZ **with** $AX = AY$, **then** $X = Y$.

A similar question arises when one considers *angles.* Suppose that a segment AB and an angle $\angle DEF$ are given. Suppose further that Mr X and Mrs Y use different methods to construct angles $\angle BAX$ and $\angle BAY$, where X and Y are both on the same side of the segment AB and $\angle BAX$ and $\angle BAY$ are both equal to the given angle $\angle DEF$.

Question
Can we be sure that A, X, Y all lie in one straight line?

Again, strictly speaking, unless we include additional axioms, the answer should be *"No. We cannot be sure"*. However, as for segments, a completely correct set of axioms would be more likely to confuse rather than to help the beginner. We shall therefore content ourselves with the following:

Axiom 4(b) If X, Y lie on the same side of line $\overleftrightarrow{AB}$ with $\angle BAX = \angle BAY$, then A, X, Y lie on one line.

This will be important when we come to prove that *Axiom 3* implies that given any line m and any point P not on m, there exists one and only one line through P which is parallel to m.

Consequence If $\angle BAX$ and $\angle BAY$ are both right angles, then X, A, Y all lie on one straight line.

Proof
If X and Y lie on the same side of $\overleftrightarrow{AB}$, this is just Axiom 4(b). Suppose that X and Y lie on opposite sides of $\overleftrightarrow{AB}$. If we extend the segment XA and choose a point Z beyond A, then $\angle XAZ$ is a straight angle, and so is equal to $\angle XAY (= \angle XAB + \angle BAY =$ two right angles). Hence Y lies on $\overleftrightarrow{XA}$. ∎

1.4   The SAS congruence axiom

Two sides and the included angle

Definition

A given triangle ABC is *congruent* to a second triangle if and only if the vertices of the second triangle can be labelled $A'B'C'$ so that $AB = A'B'$, $BC = B'C'$ and $CA = C'A'$. Also $\angle ABC = \pm\angle A'B'C'$, $\angle BCA = \pm\angle B'C'A'$ and $\angle CAB = \pm\angle C'B'A'$, where among the angle equalities *all* signs are plus or *all* signs are minus, these two possibilities corresponding to whether ABC and $A'B'C'$ have the same or *different* clockwise orderings around the two triangles.

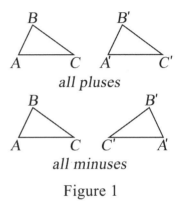

all pluses

all minuses

Figure 1

Note Intuitively we want two triangles to be *congruent* if they have exactly the *same size and shape*. Since *shape* depends on the *magnitude* of the angles rather than their orientation, we certainly want to make sure that every triangle will be congruent to one which is similar to it in all respects *except* that the angles are orientated in the opposite direction. In the language of transformations, we require that the relation of congruence should remain *invariant* under *reflections* as well as *rotations* and *translations*. The resulting invariance under all *orthogonal* transformations means that Euclidean geometry gives rise eventually (when we finally come to prove Pythagoras's theorem) to the same formula for distance that we are used to in co-ordinate geometry.

The final axiom in this introductory chapter is exceedingly powerful in that it tells us that in order to conclude that two triangles are congruent *in all respects* we only need to check *three* particular equalities among the six equalities in the above definition.

Axiom 5 (SAS Congruence) A given triangle ABC **is congruent to a second triangle if and only if there is a way of labelling the vertices of the second triangle** $A'B'C'$ **so that**

$$AB = A'B', BC = B'C' \text{ and } \angle ABC = \pm\angle A'B'C'.$$

Note The fact that the "A" in "SAS" is *between* the two "S"s reminds you that the angles in the two triangles which have to be shown to be equal before using SAS are the two angles *between* the sides which are equal in pairs.

Notation When working with a triangle labelled ABC, if we are not concerned about the *orientation* of the angles it is often convenient to abbreviate $\angle ABC$ by writing just $\angle B$. Similarly, $\angle BCA$ is denoted $\angle C$, and $\angle CAB$ is denoted $\angle A$.

Exercise 1(a)

1. Prove that the property of "congruence" is an equivalence relation on the set of triangles (that is,

    (a) that each triangle ABC is congruent to itself;

    (b) that if triangle ABC is congruent to triangle $A'B'C'$, then triangle $A'B'C'$ is also congruent to triangle ABC; and

    (c) that if triangle ABC is congruent to triangle $A'B'C'$, and triangle $A'B'C'$ is congruent to triangle $A''B''C''$, then triangle ABC is congruent to triangle $A''B''C''$).

2*. Show how to construct on a given line $\overleftrightarrow{AB}$ a point C (other than A) such that $AB = BC$.

3*. Triangle ABC is *isosceles* (with *base* BC, and *apex* A) if $AB = AC$. Suppose that you know that triangle ABC is isosceles with BC as base. If you wanted to **prove** that $\angle B$ and $\angle C$ are *necessarily* equal, which of the following "proofs" do you think is valid? (At least one of the three proofs is incorrect. Bear in mind we are trying to stick to a *logical development*, so must not use results which have not yet been proved.)

Claim $\angle B = \angle C$
Proof (i)

Consider the two triangles ABC and ACB. If we let the vertices A, C, B of the "second" triangle correspond to the vertices A, B, C of the "first" triangle *in that order*, then we have

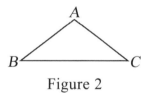

Figure 2

$$\begin{aligned} AB &= AC \quad \text{(given)}; \\ CA &= BA \quad \text{(given)}: \end{aligned}$$

and finally

$$\angle CAB = -\angle BAC$$

(common angle). The two triangles are therefore congruent *in all respects* by the SAS axiom. Hence $\angle B = \angle C$.

Proof (ii)

Let the bisector of angle $\angle BAC$ meet BC in M. Consider the two triangles BAM and CAM (with their vertices matched up in that order).

We have

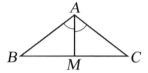

$$
\begin{aligned}
AB &= AC && \text{(given)} \\
AM &&& \text{(common side)}
\end{aligned}
$$

and finally
$\angle BAM = -\angle CAM$ (by construction).

Figure 3

Hence the two triangles are congruent in all respects by the SAS congruence axiom, so $\angle B = \angle C$.

Proof (iii)

Let P be a point on the extension of AB such that $BP = BA$ and let Q be a point on AC such that $CQ = CA$.

Then $AP = AQ$, and in the two triangles APC and AQB (with their vertices matched up in that order) we have

$$
\begin{aligned}
AP &= AQ && \text{(construction)}; \\
CA &= BA && \text{(given)}
\end{aligned}
$$

and finally $\angle PAC = -\angle QAB$ (common angle).

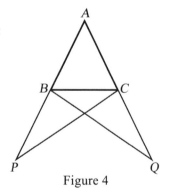

Figure 4

Hence these triangles are congruent in all respects by the SAS congruence axiom; in particular we have $\angle CPA = -\angle BQA$.

We now use the SAS congruence axiom again for the two

triangles BCP and CBQ for which we have

$$
\begin{aligned}
BC &= CB & \text{(common side)};\\
BP &= CQ & \text{(by construction)};\\
\angle CPB &= -\angle BQC & \text{(proved)}.
\end{aligned}
$$

Hence the triangles BCP and CBQ are congruent in all respects; in particular $\angle BCP = -\angle CBQ$.

But from the first pair of congruent triangles we know that $\angle ACP = -\angle ABQ$. Hence, by subtraction, we have $\angle CBA = -\angle BCA$ - that is, $\angle B = \angle C$. ∎

4*. Suppose that you know that triangles ABC and $A'BC$ are both isosceles with base BC, and that A and A' are both on the same side of the line $\overleftrightarrow{BC}$. Extend AA' to meet BC in M. Prove that the straight line $AA'M$ bisects internally both the angle at A and the angle at A'. Prove further that M is the midpoint of BC and that $AA'M$ is perpendicular to BC.

5. Give clearly explained straightedge and compass constructions

    (a) to bisect a given angle;

    (b) to find the midpoint of a line segment;

    (c) to erect a perpendicular from a point on a line;

    (d) to drop a perpendicular from a point to a line.

Use the results of Exercise 4 to prove that each of your constructions does what it is supposed to do.

1.5   The SSS congruence theorem

Three sides equal in pairs

Up to this point we knew so little that it was all too easy to slip into using results which have not yet been proved. Now, however, we are well and truly in business. For having established the basic properties of isosceles triangles, many of the results which we may have been tempted to appeal to *before they could legitimately be used* can now be properly proved. We will then be in a position to make much more rapid progress.

Exercise 1(b)

6*. Let triangle ABC be such that $\angle B = \angle C$ in magnitude. Prove that $AB = AC$.

7. (a) Explain why each of the figures below is impossible.

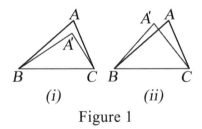

Figure 1

   (i) A' on the same side of BC as A, A' in the interior of triangle ABC, $AB = A'B$, $AC = A'C$.

   (ii) A' on the same side of BC as A, A' exterior to the triangle ABC, $AB = A'B$, $AC = A'C$.

   (b) Suppose that A and A' lie on the same side of BC with $AB = A'B$ and $AC = A'C$. Where must A' lie?

8*. **The SSS congruence theorem - three sides equal in pairs**

   Prove that if two triangles ABC and $A'B'C'$ are given such that

   $$AB = A'B', \quad BC = B'C', \quad CA = C'A',$$

   then the triangles ABC and $A'B'C'$ are congruent in all respects.

9*. Given a line m and a point P not on m, devise a straightedge and compass construction to draw a line parallel to m through the point P. You may be convinced that your construction "works", but you should find that you cannot justify it at this stage. What result must we prove before we can justify such a construction? (Come back to this after working through §1.7.)

10. Let the base BC of triangle ABC be extended to D. Prove that

   (a) $\angle DCA > \angle DBA$;

   (b) $\angle DCA > \angle BAC$.

1.6   The ASA congruence theorem

Two angles and the side between them

Theorem (ASA congruence) If triangles ABC and $A'B'C'$ are such that

$$BC = B'C', \quad \angle ABC = \pm\angle A'B'C', \quad \angle BCA = \pm\angle B'C'A'$$

where both signs are plus or both signs are minus, then triangles ABC and $A'B'C'$ are congruent.

Proof

It is enough to prove that $AB = A'B'$ (since then

$$
\begin{aligned}
AB &= A'B', \\
\angle ABC &= \pm\angle A'B'C', \\
BC &= B'C'
\end{aligned}
$$

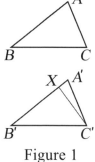

Figure 1

so the triangles are congruent by the SAS axiom).

Mark off on $\overleftrightarrow{B'A'}$ a point X (on the same side of B' as A') so that $BA = B'X$. (The diagram shows X internal to the segment $B'A'$. You should check the proof still works if X lies beyond A'.) Triangles ABC and $XB'C'$ are congruent by the SAS axiom ($AB = XB', \angle ABC = \angle A'B'C', BC = B'C'$). Hence $\angle ACB = \angle XC'B'$. But $\angle ACB = \angle A'C'B'$, so $\angle XC'B' = \angle A'C'B'$. Thus X and A' coincide, so $AB = A'B'$. ■

Note Once we have proved that the angles in a triangle add to 180°, we can immediately deduce the
SAA congruence theorem If triangles ABC and $A'B'C'$ satisfy

$$AB = A'B', \angle ABC = \angle A'B'C', \angle BCA = \angle B'C'A',$$

then the two triangles are congruent in all respects.

Proof
Once we know that the angles in any triangle add to 180°, the given information implies that

$$\begin{aligned}
\angle CAB &= \angle C'A'B' \quad \text{(deduced)};\\
AB &= A'B' \quad \text{(given)};\\
\angle BCA &= \angle B'C'A' \quad \text{(given)}.
\end{aligned}$$

Hence the SAS congruence axiom applies, so the two triangles are congruent in all respects. ∎

1.7 Proof that parallel lines exist and that angles in a triangle add to 180°.

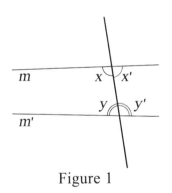

Figure 1

Suppose that two lines m and m' are crossed by a "transverse" line which creates angles x and y on one side. If these two angles add to *less than* 180°, then the parallel axiom (*Axiom 3*) guarantees that m and m' must meet on that side. If however the two angles x and y add to *more than* 180°, the two angles x' and y' on the other side of the transverse line must add to *less that* 180°, so the lines m and m' will meet on that side instead.

In **neither** case can the two lines m and m' be parallel.

Consequence If two lines m and m' are to have any chance of being parallel, the two angles x and y on one side of any transverse line must add to exactly 180°.

The next theorem establishes the converse statement: that *whenever* the angles x and y on one side of a transverse line add to exactly 180°, the two lines m and m' must be parallel.

Theorem (Condition for parallels) Distinct lines m and m' are parallel if and only if some transverse line creates interior angles x, y on one side of m adding to exactly 180°.

Note If *some* transverse line creates angles adding to 180°, then the two lines are parallel. But then, by the remarks preceding the theorem, *every* transverse line must create angles adding to 180°.

Proof

If the lines m and m' are parallel, the remarks preceding the theorem show that x and y must add to 180°. Thus the condition is *necessary*.

Now suppose some transverse line l makes internal angles x and y on one side with sum 180°. We must show that m and m' have to be parallel.

Let A, A' be the points where the line l crosses m, m' respectively. Since the angle on m at A is a straight angle, and the angle on m' at A' is a straight angle, we see that the internal angles which l makes with m and m' on the other side of line l must be y and x respectively. In particular, the two internal angles which l makes with m, m' on the other side of l also add to 180°. **Suppose that m and m' are not parallel.**

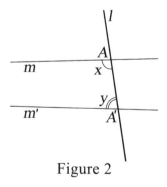

Figure 2

Then they must meet. We may suppose, without loss of generality, that they
meet at some point X on the left. We deduce a contradiction as follows. Let X'
be the point on m', on the opposite side
of l from X, with $A'X' = AX$. Then triangles AXA' and $A'X'A$ are congruent
(since we have

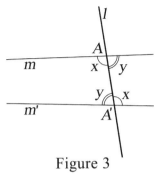

Figure 3

$$\begin{aligned} A'A &= AA' &\text{(common side),}\\ \angle A'AX &= \angle AA'X' &(= x)\\ AX &= A'X' &\text{(by construction)} \end{aligned}$$

so we may apply the SAS axiom).

But then we have

$$\angle AA'X = \angle A'AX' = y,$$

so the point X' must also lie on the
line m (by *Axiom 4(b)*), since AX' and
m are two lines which create equal angles y on the same side of the same

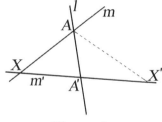

Figure 4

line segment AA' at the same point A. However, then m and m'
meet in two points X and X' on opposite sides of l contradicting
Axiom 1.

This contradiction shows that we were wrong to suppose that m
and m' are *not* parallel. Hence m and m' must be parallel. ∎

Corollary If m is any line and A' is a point not on m, then there
exists a *unique* line m' through A' parallel to m.

Proof
Drop a perpendicular from A' onto m, meeting m at the point A
(say). Let m' be the perpendicular to AA' through the point A'.

Then, by the above theorem, m' must be parallel to m. Moreover, any other line through A' which is parallel to m would have to create internal angles on each side adding to $180°$, so must be perpendicular to AA' and hence must be the same line as m'.   ■

You should now go back and finish Exercise 9.

Exercise 1(c)

11. (a) Prove that two lines m and m' are parallel if and only if for some transversal line l *corresponding* angles (that is *F-angles*) are equal.

   (b) Prove that two lines m and m' are parallel if and only if for some transversal line l *alternate* angles (that is, *Z-angles*) are equal.

12*. Prove that the angles in any triangle ABC add to $180°$.

13. Prove that in any triangle ABC, $AB > BC$ if and only if $\angle C > \angle A$.

14. Prove that in any triangle the sum of any two sides is greater than the third side.

   We need some definitions before proving the basic results on quadrilaterals.

Definitions

1. A *trapezium* is a quadrilateral in which (at least) one pair of opposite sides are parallel.

2. A *parallelogram* is a quadrilateral $ABCD$ in which the opposite sides AB, DC are parallel and the opposite sides BC, AD are also parallel.

3. A *rhombus* is a parallelogram in which two adjacent sides are equal.

4. A *rectangle* is a parallelogram in which each angle is a right angle.

5. A *square* is a rhombus which is also a rectangle.

Exercise 1(d)

15*. Prove that in a parallelogram opposite sides are equal and opposite angles are equal.

16*. Show that in the parallelogram $ABCD$, if the diagonals AC and BD meet at X, then $AX = XC$ and $BX = XD$ (that is, the diagonals of any parallelogram bisect each other).

17. Prove that the diagonals of a rectangle are equal.

18. Prove that the diagonals of a rhombus intersect at right angles.

19*. Prove that a quadrilateral in which both pairs of opposite angles are equal has to be a parallelogram.

From Exercises 15 and 19 we observe that a quadrilateral is a parallelogram **if and only if** its opposite angles are equal. We have already met a number of other instances where *both* a theorem *and* its converse are true. However, it is important to realise that such cases are the exception, rather than the rule.

It is perhaps the worst howler in geometry to prove a theorem the wrong way round, for this betrays the fact that one does not understand the distinction between a *necessary* and a *sufficient* condition. If P and Q are two conditions, then

"P is a *sufficient* condition for Q" means "if P holds, then Q *has* to hold", i.e."*P forces Q to hold*", or "$P \Rightarrow Q$". On the other hand "P is a *necessary* condition for Q" means " Q cannot hold *unless* P holds *too*", i.e."*Q forces P to hold*", or "$Q \Rightarrow P$".

So always make sure that you are proving things the right way round, and do not idly write the symbol "$\Leftrightarrow$" linking two statements unless you understand clearly why the two statements are *completely equivalent* – that is that *each statement implies the other.*

Exercise 1(e)

20. Is it true that the quadrilateral $ABCD$ is a parallelogram if and only if its diagonals AC and BD bisect each other? Justify your assertion.

21. Is it true that the quadrilateral $ABCD$ is a rhombus if and only if its diagonals AC and BD are perpendicular to each other? Justify your assertion.

    Remember In order to prove that a statement is *false* you only need *just one counter-example,* no matter how trivial it may seem.

22. (a) Is it true that distinct straight lines l and m are parallel if and only if whenever l' is perpendicular to l and m' is perpendicular to m, either $l' = m'$ or l' and m' are parallel? Justify your assertion.

    (b) Is it true that if AB and BC are two line segments and A, B, C are not on a straight line, then the perpendicular bisectors of AB and BC necessarily meet?

1.8 Area

We take for granted the basic fact that

if $ABCD$ is a rectangle with $AB = w$ and $BC = h$, then area $(ABCD) = wh$.

We shall also take it for granted that the areas of congruent shapes are equal, and that the area of a compound figure is equal to the sum of the areas of the constituent parts.

Let $ABCD$ be a parallelogram. Drop the perpendiculars from D and C onto the line $\overleftrightarrow{AB}$, to meet this line at A' and B' respectively.

Now

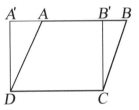

Figure 1

$$\begin{aligned} \angle A'AD &= 180^\circ - \angle DAB \\ &= \angle ABC \quad (ABCD \text{ is a parallelogram}) \\ &= \angle B'BC. \end{aligned}$$

Similarly $\angle ADA' = \angle BCB'$ *(Check this!)*.

Since $AD = BC$ (opposite sides of a parallelogram), it follows that triangles $AA'D$ and $BB'C$ are congruent. Hence

$$\begin{aligned} \text{area } (ABCD) &= \text{area } (AB'CD) + \text{area } (BB'C) \\ &= \text{area } (AB'CD) + \text{area } (AA'D) \\ &= \text{area } (A'B'CD) \\ &= (A'D)(DC). \end{aligned}$$

Thus we have proved the following theorem.

Theorem
The area of a parallelogram is equal to the length of any side chosen as base multiplied by the perpendicular distance between the base and the opposite side. *(That is, area equals base times height.)*

Corollary Given any triangle ABC, if we choose any side, say AB, as base, and if the perpendicular from C to $\overleftrightarrow{AB}$ meets $\overleftrightarrow{AB}$ in the point C', then we have

$$\text{area}\,(ABC) = \frac{1}{2}(AB).(CC').$$

(That is, area equals half base times height.)

Proof
Given the triangle ABC, draw the line through A parallel to BC and the line through C parallel to AB. Let these lines meet at the point D. Then triangles ABC and CDA are congruent by $ASA(\,\angle BAC = \angle DCA$ (alternate angles), $AC = CA$ (common side), and $\angle ACB = \angle CAD$ (alternate angles), so area $(ABC) =$ area (CDA) and area $(ABCD) =$ area $(ABC) +$ area (CDA) $= 2\times$ area (ABC). ∎

1.9 Theorem of Pythagoras (fl. 530 BC)

Theorem
In any right angled triangle with sides of length x, y, z, where z is the length of the side opposite the right angle, we have $x^2 + y^2 = z^2$.

Proof

Let $ABCD$ be a square of side $x + y$. Let P, Q, R, S be points on AB, BC, CD, DA respectively, such that

$$AP = BQ = CR = DS = x.$$

Let $PQ = z$.

Prove in the following order:

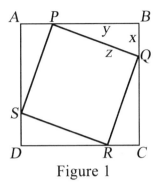

Figure 1

1. Triangles APS and BQP are congruent.

2. $\angle SPQ = 90^{\circ}$.

3. $PQRS$ is a square.

4. $x^2 + y^2 = z^2$ (consider the area of $ABCD$ in two different ways).

There are many other elegant and correct proofs of Pythagoras's theorem.

Notation In a triangle ABC, we usually denote the length if the side opposite vertex A by a, the length of the side opposite vertex B by b, and the length of the side opposite vertex C by c.

Exercise 1(f)

23. Let ABC be a triangle with angles at B and at C both $\leq 90^{\circ}$. Let the perpendicular from A to BC have length h and meet BC at the point D. If $CD = d$, show that $c^2 = a^2 + b^2 - 2ad$. Hence conclude that $c^2 = a^2 + b^2$ only when the angle at C in a right angle.

24. Let ABC be a triangle in which the angle at C is $\geq 90^o$. Show in a similar way to Exercise 23 that $c^2 = a^2 + b^2$ only when the angle at C is a right angle.

25*. **(Converse of Pythagoras's theorem)** Prove that if the sides of triangle ABC satisfy $a^2 + b^2 = c^2$, then the triangle has a right angle at C.

1.10 Additional problems on Chapter 1

26*. Prove that a quadrilateral $ABCD$ in which $AB = BC = CD = DA$ must be a rhombus.

   Definition Given two points A, X the *half-line* $\overrightarrow{AX}$ consists of all points on the line $\overleftrightarrow{AX}$ which lie on the same side of A as X does.

27. Let $\overrightarrow{AX}, \overrightarrow{AY}$ be distinct half-lines with a common endpoint A. Prove that the perpendicular distances from a point P onto these half-lines are equal if and only if P lies on the angle bisector of $\angle XAY$.

28*. Given a triangle ABC, prove that the perpendicular bisectors of the sides of triangle ABC meet at a point equidistant from the three vertices.

29. In the triangle ABC, let L, M be the midpoints of the sides BC, CA respectively. Prove that $AL = BM$ if and only if $AC = BC$.

30*. P, Q, R are points on the sides BC, CA, AB of triangle ABC Prove that the perpendiculars to the sides at these points meet in a common point if and only if

$$BP^2 + CQ^2 + AR^2 = PC^2 + QA^2 + RB^2.$$

31*. Given a triangle ABC, let L, M, N be the feet of the perpendiculars from a point K to the sides BC, CA, AB respectively. Prove that the perpendiculars from A, B, C to MN, NL, LM respectively are concurrent (that is, meet in a common point).

32. Given a triangle ABC, let P, Q, R be the feet of the perpendiculars from a point S to the sides BC, CA, AB respectively. L, M, N are the midpoints, respectively, of these sides. Prove that

$$(LP)(BC) + (MQ)(CA) + (NR)(AB) = 0.$$

33. Let X, Y, Z be the midpoints of the sides AB, BC, CA of the triangle ABC. Let P be defined on BC so that $\angle CPZ = \angle YXZ$.
Prove that AP is perpendicular to BC.

34. A point O is taken within a convex polygon $ABC \ldots KL$. Prove that $(OA + OB + OC + \ldots + OK + OL)$ is greater that the semi-perimeter of the polygon.

35*. Two triangles $ABC, A'BC$ have the same base and the same height (that is, the line $\overleftrightarrow{AA'}$ is parallel to the base BC). Through the point P where their sides intersect we draw a straight line parallel to the base; this line meets the other side of ABC in X and the other side of $A'BC$ in X'.
Prove that $XP = X'P$.

36*. In a right angled triangle prove that the straight line joining the right angle to the centre of the square to the hypotenuse always bisects the right angle.

1.11   Hints to starred problems, and answers to other problems (where needed)

2. This is something to do with circles.

3. (ii) is invalid in the sense that we have not yet explained *how* to bisect an angle.

4. These results are very important. Given the path we have chosen so far, there is only one correct way through. First, why is it possible to use a figure with A' an internal point of triangle ABC ? Once you have settled this, prove that $\angle A'BA = -\angle A'CA$. Next you have to use the SAS axiom (if only because this is the only congruence result you can use at this stage) to prove that triangles ABA' and ACA' are congruent. This proves that AA' bisects $\angle A$ internally. Now use SAS to prove that triangles BAM and CAM are congruent. You should then be able to complete the problem.

6. If $AC > AB$ (say), let the perpendicular from the midpoint of BC meet AC in N. Now think about triangle NBC.

9. Drop the perpendicular from P to m and extend this line backwards. Then erect a perpendicular at P on the line just drawn. But why does it work? *You will have to come back to this later.*

12. In triangle ABC draw a line through A parallel to BC; then use Exercise 11(ii).

15. Draw a diagonal and use ASA congruence.

16. Prove that triangles AXB and CXD are congruent, using the result of Exercise 15 and ASA congruence.

19. Prove first that the angles of any quadrilateral sum to 360°. Then a pair of consecutive angles sum to what?

20. Yes.

21. No; consider the figure generally called a *kite*.

22. (a) Yes. (b) Yes.

25. Construct B' on the opposite side of AC to B with $AB' = AB$ and $B'C = BC$. Then ABC is congruent to $AB'C$ (by Pythagoras and SSS). Therefore ...

26. Draw a diagonal and use SSS congruence to show that $ABCD$ is a parallelogram.

28. You need to use the second part of Exercise 22 to get started. Then let two of the perpendicular bisectors meet at O, and prove that $OA = OB = OC$. Now think about the perpendicular from O onto the other side.

30. Prove the "only if" part first using Pythagoras's theorem several times. You will need this part to prove the "if" part; this is similar to the method of Exercise 28.

31. This is a problem using the theorem of Exercise 30.

35. This should be done by considering areas, and you will have to use (and should strictly first *prove*) the formula for the area of a trapezium.

36. Look at the figure used for proving Pythagoras's theorem.

"[Are] the axioms of geometry experimental truths?

We do not experiment with ideal straight lines or perfect circles; that can only be done with material objects. On what then could one base experiments that might serve as the foundation of geometry?

We [. . .] constantly reason as if geometric figures behaved like solid objects. Perhaps geometry borrows from experience the properties of such bodies?

But a difficulty remains, and is insurmountable. If geometry were an experimental science, it would not be an exact science, but would be subject to continual revision. Nay, it would from this very day be convicted of error, since we know there is no rigorously rigid solid.

The axioms of geometry are [. . .] neither synthetic a priori judgements nor experimental facts.
*They are **conventions**; our choice among all possible conventions is **guided** by experimental facts; but it remains **free** and is limited only by the necessity of avoiding all contradiction. Thus it is that the postulates can remain **rigorously** true even though the experimental laws which have determined their adoption are only approximately true.*

. . . the axioms of geometry [. . .] are merely diguised definitions.

Then what are we to think of the question: Is Euclidean geometry true?
It has no meaning.
*One may as well ask whether the metric system is true and the old measures false; whether cartesian co-ordinates are true and polar co-ordinates false. One geometry cannot be more true than another; it can only be **more convenient** (or more **appropriate**).*

Now, Euclidean geometry is, and will remain, the most convenient:
(i) Because it is the simplest; and it is so not only in consequence

of our mental habits, or of I know not what direct intuition we may have of Euclidean space; it is the simplest in itself, just as a polynomial of first degree is simpler than one of the second degree; the formulas of spherical trigonometry are more complicated than those of plane trigonometry, and they would still appear so to an analyst ignorant of their geometric significance.

(ii) Because it accords sufficiently well with the properties of natural solids, those bodies which our hands and our eyes compare and with which we make our instruments of measure."

(Henri Poincaré 1854-1912)

Chapter 2

Similar Triangles and Trigonometry

2.1 Similarity and proportion: angles and lengths

In Chapter 1 we introduced the *axioms* on which our approach to Euclidean geometry is to be based. These axioms specified the basic properties of *points, lines, angles, line segments, triangles,* and the connections between them. In this chapter we look at a more subtle, yet very important, way in which the angles and the sides of a triangle are connected.

Definition Two triangles are *similar* if and only if their vertices can be labelled A, B, C and A', B', C' so that

$$\angle ABC = \pm\angle A'B'C', \quad \angle BCA = \pm\angle B'C'A', \quad \angle CAB = \pm C'A'B',$$

where all three signs are the same (either all plus or all minus). Though the definition insists that all three pairs of angles match up, we know that it is enough to check just *two* pairs of angles (since two angles in any triangle determine the third angle, by Exercise 1.12).

Consequence To prove that two triangles are similar we only have to match up *two* of the angles in one triangle with *two* of the angles in the other.

The above definition of similar triangles should be familiar. Indeed, it may be *too* familiar in the sense that you may assume it says *more* than it really does. The point we wish to stress here is that all we know about similar triangles is that their *angles* match up in pairs. In particular, the definition doesn't even mention the *sides* of the two triangles! Thus, if we know that two triangles are similar, *there is no a priori reason to believe that we can conclude anything at all about the sides of the two triangles.*

The fact that given two similar triangles we *can* in fact conclude something interesting about the sides is not at all obvious, and is the main result of this chapter.

To make this distinction as clear as we can we introduce explicitly the idea of *proportional* triangles - as a different concept with its own independent definition involving only *ratios of lengths*.

Definition Two triangles are *proportional* if and only if their vertices can be labelled A, B, C and A', B', C' so that corresponding sides are in the same ratio:

$$AB \ : \ A'B' \ = \ BC : \ B'C' \ = \ CA : C'A' \ = k \ : \ 1$$

for some constant k. The constant k is called the *enlargement factor, scale factor* or *magnification factor* of triangle ABC relative to triangle $A'B'C'$.

The main goal of this chapter is to prove that similarity can be detected equally well by comparing angles or by comparing sides.

Two triangles are similar if and only if thcy are proportional.

Before reading any further, you might like to take time out to try to think ahead and try to see which of the ideas we met in Chapter 1 are going to allow us to use the information that

the *angles* in two triangles are equal in pairs (similarity)

to prove that

corresponding *sides* are in the same ratio (proportionality),

and conversely.

2.2 From Pythagoras (fl. 530 BC) to Eudoxus (fl. 370 BC)

In Chapter 1 we stated that whenever we are given two segments AB and PQ, we can determine the *ratio* of the two segments

$$AB : PQ.$$

We hinted that there were logical difficulties when this ratio was not *rational*; but we did not go into details.

Since the definition of *proportional* triangles depends so heavily on the ratios of the sides of the two triangles, this may be an appropriate place to take a closer look at some of the problems surrounding the simple-minded approach to ratio.

The early Pythagoreans believed that the ratio of any two line segments would always correspond to the ratio of two *whole* numbers. More precisely, they believed that, given any two line line segments AB and PQ, it would always be possible to find a sufficiently small *common unit XY* which would measure both segments *exactly*. In other words, they believed that, one could always choose a unit XY so that for some (possibly very large) whole numbers m and n you could *simultaneously* divide AB into exactly m copies of the chosen unit XY, and PQ into exactly n copies of XY; the ratio $AB : PQ$ would then be equal to a ratio of *whole* numbers $m : n$.

Though this "belief" turned out to be mistaken, it should not be dismissed too lightly. For it is part and parcel of an underlying philosophy which lies at the root of much of modern science, namely that the world of thought and the world of nature are bound together by the world of *number*, and that the world of number is rooted in the *whole* numbers.

We know that the Pythagoreans came to realise their mistake, though we do not know exactly when or how this happened. Later generations of Greeks used the following example as the standard way of illustrating ratios which were *not* ratios of *whole* numbers, so this may have been how the mistake was originally discovered. (For two other examples that were well known in the ancient world, see Exercises 1 and 2.)

Theorem
In any square $ABCD$, the ratio $AC : AB$ of a diagonal AC to a side AB cannot be a ratio of whole numbers.

Proof
We prove that the diagonal AC and the side AB can have no common unit of measure.

We begin the proof by supposing the *contrary* - namely that such a common measure *does* exist - and deduce a *contradiction*. From this it then follows that the original supposition must have been false.

Suppose that AC and AB can be measured *exactly* with some sufficiently small common unit XY.

Then each of AB, AC is an integral number times the supposed unit XY – say $AB = mXY$, $AC = nXY$. Mark off B' on CA so that $B'C = AB$. Then draw $B'C'$ through B' perpendicular to AC to meet AB at C'.

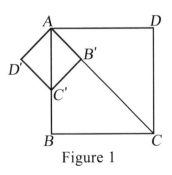

Figure 1

The angles of triangle $AB'C'$ are $45°, 90°, 45°$, so $B'C' = B'A$. We can now complete the new square $AB'C'D'$.

The sides of this square have length

$$AB' = AC - B'C = AC - BC = (n - m)XY,$$

Thus if AC and BC are both integer multiples of the supposed common unit XY, their difference AB' is still an integer number times *the same unit XY* – though the integer multiple is now much smaller than it was for the side AB of the original square.

In the two right angled triangles CBC' and $CB'C'$, CC' is a common side and $B'C = BC$ by construction. Applying Pythagoras's theorem to each triangle then shows that $B'C' = BC'$. This fact allows us to find the length of the diagonal AC' of the new square:

$$AC' = AB - BC' = AB - B'C' = AB - AB'$$

$$= AB - (AC - BC) = 2AB - AC = (2m - n)XY$$

Thus if AC and BC are both integer multiples of the supposed common unit XY, then $AC'(= 2AB - AC)$ is still an integer number times *the same unit XY*.

Therefore XY is a common measure for the diagonal AC' and side AB' of the new square.

Moreover, the side of the new square is $BC' = B'C'$, which is less than the diagonal AC'. Hence BC' is less than half BA $(= BC' + C'A)$.

Therefore the side $B'C'$ of the new square is less than half the side AB of the old one.

Suppose we now start with the new square $AB'C'D'$, whose side and diagonal still have the original unit XY as a common measure, and repeat the process to get a third square $AB''C''D''$. As before, the sides of the square $AB''C''D''$ will be less than half as long as the sides of the square $AB'C'D'$, and the same unit XY will still be a common measure of the side and diagonal of the new square.

If we continue in this way, we obtain a whole sequence of squares. Each of these squares has the original unit XY as a common measure for its side and diagonal. Yet each square in the sequence has sides which are less than half as long as the sides of the previous square. Hence we must eventually produce a square whose sides are *shorter than XY and so cannot be measured by the line segment XY!*

This contradiction shows that our original supposition must have been wrong: that is, the side and diagonal of the original square $ABCD$ can have no common measure, so the ratio $AC : BC$ is *not rational.* ∎

Pythagorean geometry had been rooted in the assumption that everything could be described in terms of whole numbers. Their proofs took it for granted that any two magnitudes of the same kind (for example, two line segments, or two areas) had a common measure which fitted into each an *exact whole* number of times. Once this fact was seen to be false, everything was called into question. It was not just their *results* and *proofs* which could no longer be trusted. They had to find a new approach to the very idea of *ratio* – preferably an approach which would allow existing results to be rescued.

This remarkable salvage job is usually attributed to Eudoxus of Cnidus around 370 BC. Eudoxus's insight was to realise that one does not need to say exactly what a ratio *is*: one only needs to know when two ratios are *equal*, or when one is *bigger* than another.

That is, Eudoxus realised that we do not need to say exactly what a ratio *is*, we only need to know *how it behaves.* You might like to compare Eudoxus's insight with Hilbert's declaration, made nearly 2300 years later, which we discussed in Chapter 1, §1.2.

Eudoxus's definition. Let a, b be magnitudes of one kind and c, d be magnitudes of another (possibly the same) kind.

Equality of ratios: we have $a : b = c : d$ precisely when for all pairs of positive integers m, n the value of $na - mb$ is positive, zero or negative according as $nc - md$ is positive, zero or negative.

Inequality of ratios: we have $a : b \neq c : d$ precisely when for some pair of integers m, n, the quantity $na - mb$ is positive while $nc - md$ is negative.

The remarkable thing about this definition is that it salvaged not only the Pythagorean's results, but also their philosophy in that it is framed solely in terms of *whole* numbers. A similar idea was used by Richard Dedekind (1831-1916) in the nineteenth century to give a construction of the real number system assuming only the existence of integers.

The "magnitudes" a, b, c, d in Eudoxus's definition are meant to be geometrical entities, *not numbers*. Strictly speaking one should distinguish clearly between geometrical *magnitudes* (such as line segments, angles and regions) and their *measures* (with respect to some chosen unit). However, excessively scrupulous application of this principle leads to complications which are *logical* (or even *linguistic*) rather than *geometrical*, and which we prefer to avoid.

Exercise 2(a)

1. Let ABC be $30°$ - $60°$ - $90°$ triangle with a right angle at C.

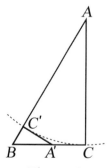

Show that the two shorter sides AC, CB have no common measure.

(Suppose AC and CB have some common measure XY. Let the circle with centre A which passes through C meet AB at C'. Let the perpendicular to AB at C' meet BC in A'.

Figure 2

(a) Show that $A'B'C'$ is also a $30°$-$60°$-$90°$ triangle.

(b) Show that $BC' = 2CB - AC$.

(c) Show that $A'C' = 2AC - 3CB$ (use $A'C' = A'C$).

(d) Hence conclude that $A'C'$ and $C'B$ also have XY as a common measure.

(e) Show that $C'A' < \frac{1}{2}CA$. Hence derive a contradiction.)

2.* Let $ABCDE$ be a regular pentagon.

Show that the diagonal AC and side AB have no common measure. (Suppose AC and AB have some common measure XY.

(a) Show that $ABCQ$ and $ABPE$ are both rhombuses. Conclude that CQ, and hence PQ, must be an integer multiple of XY.

(b) Show that $RTCP$ is a rhombus. Conclude that RT must be an integer multiple of XY.

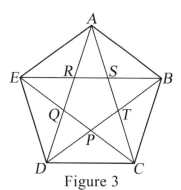

Figure 3

Hence derive a contradiction as in the proof for the square.)

2.3 The basic results about similarity

The main theorem of this chapter is that two triangles are similar if and only if they are proportional. Before proving this result (Theorem 5) we prove four other important theorems, numbered Theorems 1-4 so that we can refer to them more easily later.

Theorem 1

If ABC is a triangle and D, E are points on AB, AC such that DE is parallel to BC, then $AD : AB = AE : AC$.

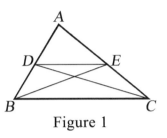

Figure 1

Note Since DE is parallel to BC we have $\angle ADE = \angle ABC$, $\angle AED = \angle ACB$, and also the angle $\angle DAE = \angle BAC$ is common. Hence the hypothesis in Theorem 1 implies that triangles ADE and ABC are *similar*. On the other hand, if we had been told instead that the two triangles were similar, with $\angle ADE = \angle ABC$ and $\angle AED = \angle ACB$, it would follow that DE was parallel to BC. Hence the hypothesis in the theorem is equivalent to the assumption that *triangles ADE and ABC are similar*, and the conclusion is that the two pairs of sides AD, AB and AE, AC are "proportional".

In Theorem 3 we shall prove, under the same hypothesis, that the two triangles ADE and ABC are actually *proportional*: i.e. the third pair of sides DE, BC are proportional with the same scale factor as AD, AB and AE, AC.

Proof of Theorem 1

Join BE and DC. Now triangles DEB and DEC have the same base DE and lie between the same parallels (DE and BC), so they have the same height. Hence triangles DEB and DEC have equal areas. Adding triangle ADE to each it follows that triangles ABE and ACD have the same area.

Therefore

$$\text{area}(ADE) : \text{area}(ABE) = \text{area}(ADE) : \text{area}(ACD).$$

If we think of the two triangles on the LHS as having bases AD and BC on the same line, we see that they have the same height.

Hence the ratio of their areas is equal to the ratio of their bases. That is, LHS = $AD : AB$. Similarly RHS = $AE : AC$, so the previous equation becomes $AD : AB = AE : AC$. ∎

Theorem 2 (Converse of Theorem 1)

If ABC is a triangle and D, E are points on the lines AB, AC respectively such that $AD : AB = AE : AC$, then DE is parallel to BC.

Proof

Draw a line through D parallel to BC, and let this meet AC at E'. We must show that $E = E'$. By Theorem 1, $AD : AB = AE' : AC$ But $AD : AB = AE : AC$ (given). Hence $AE' = AE$ so E' and E coincide. ∎

The next theorem completes the missing conclusion from Theorem 1.

Theorem 3

Let ABC be a triangle and let D, E be points on AB and AC respectively such that $AD : AB = AE : AC = k : 1$. Then also $DE : BC = k : 1$.

Proof

We know from Theorem 2 that DE is parallel to BC. Draw the line through E parallel to AB to meet BC in F. Next draw the line through F parallel to CA to meet AB in G. Then $DEFB$ and $AEFG$ are both parallelograms. Hence

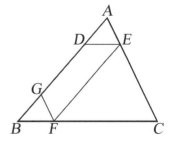

Figure 2

$$AD = AG - DG = EF - DG = DB - DG = GB,$$

since opposite sides of a parallelogram are equal. Now GF is parallel to AC, so by Theorem 1 we have $BF : BC = BG : BA$. Hence $DE : BC = BF : BC = BG : BA = AD : AB = k : 1$ as required. ∎

Theorem 4 (SAS version of similarity)

Two triangles are similar if and only if their vertices can be labelled ABC and $A'B'C'$ so that

$$\angle CAB = \pm\angle C'A'B', \quad \text{and} \quad A'B' : AB = A'C' : AC \qquad (*)$$

Proof

Suppose first that we have two similar triangles. Then, by definition, their vertices can be labelled ABC and $A'B'C'$ so that

$$\angle CAB = \pm\angle C'A'B', \quad \angle ABC = \pm\angle A'B'C', \quad BCA = \pm\angle B'C'A',$$

where all signs are plus or all signs are minus. Hence the first of the three conditions in $(*)$ certainly holds.

Construct a triangle $AB''C''$ with B'' lying on AB and C'' lying on AC, such that $AB'' = A'B'$ and $AC'' = A'C'$.

Then triangles $A'B'C'$ and $A''B''C$ are congruent (by SAS). It follows that $\angle AB''C''$ and $\angle ABC$ are equal, so $B''C''$ is parallel to BC. Hence $AB'' : AB = AC'' : AC$ (by Theorem 1), so the last two conditions in $(*)$ also hold.

Now suppose that we have two triangles which can be labelled so that the three conditions in $(*)$ hold.

We suppose first that $\angle CAB = +\angle C'A'B'$ and show how to use the same idea as in the previous part to prove that $\angle ABC = \angle A'B'C'$, $\angle BCA = \angle B'C'A'$.

Construct a triangle $AB''C''$ with B'' lying on AB and C'' lying on AC, such that $AB'' = A'B', AC'' = A'C'$. Then the triangles $A'B'C'$ and $AB''C''$ are congruent (by SAS). Now $AB'' = A'B'$ and $AC'' = A'C'$, so $AB'' : AB = AC'' : AC$ (given). Hence $B''C''$ is parallel to BC (by Theorem 2), so $\angle AB''C'' = \angle ABC$

and $\angle AC''B'' = \angle ACB$. It then follows that $\angle A'B'C' = \angle ABC$ and $\angle A'C'B' = \angle ACB$ (since triangles $A'B'C'$ and $AB''C''$ are congruent), so triangles ABC and $A'B'C'$ are *similar*.

Finally if $\angle CAB = -\angle C'A'B'$, construct a triangle $AB''C''$ with B'' lying on AB and C'' lying on AC, such that $AB'' = A'B', AC'' = A'C'$. Then triangles $A'B'C'$ and $AB''C''$ are again congruent by SAS, with the two corresponding angles having opposite sign. Thus the angles in triangle $AB''C''$ all have the opposite sign to those in triangle $A'B'C'$. Now $AB'' = A'B'$ and $AC'' = A'C'$, so $AB'' : AB = AC'' : AC$ (given).

Hence $B''C''$ is parallel to BC (by Theorem 2), so $\angle AB''C'' = \angle ABC$ and $\angle AC''B'' = \angle ACB$. It then follows that $\angle A'B'C' = -\angle ABC$ and $\angle A'C'B' = -\angle ACB$ (since triangles $A'B'C'$ and $AB''C''$ are congruent), so finally we have established that triangles ABC and $A'B'C'$ are *similar*. ∎

The SAS version of similarity is perhaps *the* most frequently used result in the solution of geometry problems.

Once we have proved (in Theorem 5) that two triangles are similar if and only if they are proportional, you will have three standard ways of recognising similar triangles, or of interpreting the fact that two triangles are known to be similar:

> AAA (the definition of similarity)
> SAS (Theorem 3), and
> SSS (proportionality, Theorem 5).

You will need to know how to use all three of these as required.

Theorem 5 (SSS version of similarity)

(i) If triangles $ABC, A'B'C'$ are similar, then they are proportional.

(ii) If triangles $ABC, A'B'C'$ are proportional, then they are similar.

Proof

(i) Suppose that triangles $ABC, A'B'C'$ are similar, and that the angles match up as $\angle ABC = \angle A'B'C'$, $\angle BCA = \angle B'C'A'$, and $\angle CAB = \angle C'A'B'$.

Mark off a point D on AB such that $AD = A'B'$, and mark a point E on AC such that $AE = A'C'$. Then the triangles ADE and $A'B'C'$ are congruent (SAS), so $DE = B'C'$, $\angle ADE = \angle A'B'C'$, and $\angle AED = \angle A'C'B'$. It follows that $\angle ADE = \angle ABC$ and $\angle AED = \angle ACB$ since triangles ABC and $A'B'C'$ are similar. Hence DE is parallel to BC, so triangles ABC and ADE are proportional by Theorems 1 and 3. If k is the scale factor for these two triangles, then triangles ABC and $A'B'C'$ are proportional with the same scale factor k (since ADE and $A'B'C'$ are congruent).

(ii) Suppose that triangles ABC and $A'B'C'$ are proportional. That is,

$$B'C' : BC = A'B' : AB = A'C' : AC.$$

Again mark off the point D on AB such that $AD = A'B'$, and mark E on AC such that $AE = A'C'$. Then

$$A'C' : AC = AE : AC = A'B' : AB = AD : AB.$$

Moreover, by Theorem 3, $AD : AB = DE : BC$.

Putting all these results together we have $DE : BC = B'C' : BC$, from which it follows that $DE = B'C'$. Hence triangles ADE and $A'B'C'$ are congruent (SSS). In particular, corresponding angles in triangles ADE and $A'B'C'$ are equal, so triangles ADE and $A'B'C'$ are similar.

On the other hand, since $AD : AB = AE : AC$, Theorem 2 implies that DE is parallel to BC so that corresponding angles in triangles ADE and ABC are also equal, so triangles ADE and ABC are similar. Hence triangles $A'B'C'$ and ABC are similar. ∎

Similarity is the most important, and the most powerful single concept in elementary geometry. Many results do not depend on the "scale", or actual size, of a figure, but only on its "shape". And in a complicated arrangement of points, lines, and circles, one often finds triangles of different sizes which happen to have equal angles. Moreover,

> whenever a problem is expressed, or can be rephrased, in terms of ratios, you can be fairly sure its solution depends on finding and exploiting similar figures.

One particular consequence of all this deserves special mention. Suppose ABC and $A'B'C'$ are *right angled* triangles, right angled at A and A', and having $\angle ABC = \angle A'B'C' = \theta$ (say). Then clearly $\angle BCA = \angle B'C'A'$ so the two triangles are *similar*, and hence also *proportional* (by Theorem 5). Hence

$$AB : A'B' = BC : B'C' = CA : C'A',$$

from which it follows that

$$AC \cdot BC = A'C' : B'C',$$

so this ratio depends only on the angle θ and not on the size of the right angled triangles ABC; we are therefore justified in using a notation for this ratio which depends only on θ – namely $\sin\theta$. Similarly,

$$BA : BC = B'A' : B'C'$$

depends only on θ, so we are justified in writing this ratio as a function of θ irrespective of the size of the triangle – namely as $\cos\theta$. In the second part of this chapter we pursue these ideas by beginning the study of trigonometry (a subject which may be seen as a systematic way of exploiting similarity).

Before we leave Theorem 5 it is important to realise that it only applies to triangles: our definition of *similarity* as "corroponding angles equal in pairs" and our definition or *proportionality* as "corresponding sides in the same ratio" are equivalent only for triangles. Polygons with more than three sides may have corresponding angles equal in pairs and yet have very different shapes: for example, any two rectangles have their angles equal in pairs, but their sides will usually be unrelated! Conversely, two polygons with more than three sides may have corresponding sides in the same ratio without having corresponding angles equal in pairs: for example, a rhombus has all its sides of equal length, so any two rhombuses can be labelled so that the ratios of corresponding sides are equal, though their angles may be quite different. There is only one way out of this: if we want "similar" and "proportional" to be equivalent for polygons with more than three sides, we have to incorporate both these properties into the definition.

Definition Two polygons with n sides, where $n > 3$, will be called *similar* precisely when they can be labelled $A_1, A_2, \ldots, A_n$ and $A'_1, A'_2, \ldots, A'_n$ in such a way that corresponding angles are equal and each pair of corresponding sides are in the same ratio.

Exercise 2(b)

3*. Prove that if you are given the lengths AB, BC, CD, DA, and $\angle DAB$, then exactly two quadrilaterals $ABCD$ can be constructed (up to congruence) where C, A are either on the same or opposite sides of the line BD. Hence write down a set of minimum information sufficient to ensure that two such quadrilaterals $ABCD$ and $A'B'C'D'$ are similar.

2.4 Worked examples

If the three results in this section *and their proofs* are familiar, you only need to read them (for revision purposes) and proceed to the Exercises that follow. However, most of those working through this material will not be in this position! For them the best strategy for each result is

- first read and make sure you understand what it is saying;

- then close the book and try to prove the result on your own as though it were an exercise:

- when you have either succeeded or got stuck, go back and compare your method, or attempt, with the method used here.

1. **Theorem** Let ABC be any triangle and let L, M, N be the midpoints of BC, CA, AB respectively. Then AL, BM, CN are concurrent - that is they all pass through a single point - at a point G, such that $AG : GL = BG : GM = CG : GN = 2 : 1$. G is called the *centroid* of the triangle ABC.

Proof

Let CN meet BM at G. Since

$$AN : AB = AM : AC = 1 : 2,$$

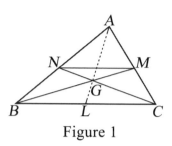

Figure 1

it follows from Theorems 2 and 3 that NM is parallel to BC and that $NM : BC = 1 : 2$. Now in triangles NMG and CBG we have $\angle NMG = \angle CBG$ (alternate angles) and $\angle NGM = \angle CGB$ (opposite angles), so triangles NMG and CBG are similar. Hence

$$CG : GN = BC : MN = 2 : 1.$$

Similarly $BG : GM = 2 : 1$.

Now let CN and AL meet at G'. Then by an analogous argument $CG' : G'N = AG' : G'L = 2 : 1$. But CGN and $CG'N$ are the same straight line, so G and G' coincide.

2. **Problem** A point P is given on the side AB of triangle ABC such that $AP < PB$. Show how to construct the line through P which bisects the area of the triangle.

Solution

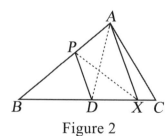

Figure 2

Let X be the point where this (unknown) line meets BC. We construct the point X in two steps. First construct the midpoint D of BC. Then join PD and construct the line through A parallel to PD. We claim that this line meets BC in the required point X, so PX is the required line. To see this, observe that

$$\text{area } (ABD) = \frac{1}{2} \text{ area } (ABC)$$

(since D is the midpoint of BC), and

$$\text{area } (APD) = \text{ area } (XPD)$$

(both have base PD and lie between parallels PD, AX). Hence

$$\frac{1}{2} \text{ area } (ABC) = \text{ area } (ABD)$$

$$= \text{ area } (ABD) - \text{ area } (APD) + \text{ area } (XPD)$$

$$= \text{ area } (PBX).$$

Moreover, since $AP < PB$, X is an interior point of BC. ∎

3. **Problem** If $ABCD$ is a parallelogram and P, Q (positioned as shown in the diagram) are such that triangles PAB and BCQ are similar, prove that each is similar to triangle PDQ.

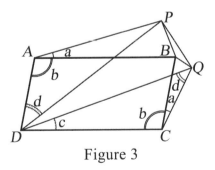

Figure 3

Solution To say that "triangles PAB and BCQ are similar" means precisely that $\angle PAB = \angle BCQ = a$ say, $\angle ABP = \angle CQB$ and $\angle BPA = \angle QBC$. Moreover, we know also that $PA/BC = AB/CQ$ (since the two triangles are automatically proportional). In the parallelogram we know that $BC = AD$ and $AB = DC$, so we have $PA/AD = DC/CQ$. Since opposite angles in a parallelogram are equal we have $\angle BAD = \angle DCB = b$ say, so $\angle DAP = \angle DCQ = a + b$. Hence, using the SAS version of similarity (Theorem 3), triangles PAD and DCQ are similar, so $\angle DPA = \angle QDC = c$ say, and $\angle ADP = \angle CQD = d$ say. From triangle DCQ we have $a + b + c + d = 180^o$ (angles in a triangle). Since $\angle ADC + \angle BCD = 180^o$ (adjacent angles in a parallelogram), we conclude that $\angle PDQ = a$. Since triangles PAD and DCQ are similar, we have $PA/PD = DC/DQ = AB/DQ$, so $PA/AB = PD/DQ$. Finally, since $\angle PAB = \angle PDQ = a$, we conclude that triangles PAB and PDQ are similar (SAS version of similarity). ∎

Exercise 2(c)

4. Triangles ABC and $A'B'C'$ are similar and $AB = kA'B'$. Prove that

$$\text{area } (ABC) = k^2 \text{ area } (A'B'C').$$

5. Given any triangle ABC prove that there exists a triangle DEF similar to it for which

$$\text{area } (DEF) = 1(DE + EF + FD)$$

   where 1 stands for the unit of length and has been included to make the equation "dimensionally" correct.

6. (This is problem 35 of Chapter 1; it is included here to encourage you to give a different solution using the ideas of Chapter 2). Two triangles ABC and $A'BC$ have the same base BC and lie between the two parallel lines BC and AA'. Through the point P where their sides intersect we draw a straight line parallel to the base; this line meets the other side of ABC in X and the other side of $A'BC$ in X'. Prove that $XP = X'P$.

7*. Three parallel lines are such that one passes through each vertex of the triangle ABC. The line through A meets BC (extended if necessary) in X, and the lines through B and C meet CA and AB (extended if necessary) in Y and Z respectively. Prove that

$$\text{area } (XYZ) = 2 \text{ area } (ABC).$$

8. Using the notation established in Worked Example 1, prove that area (BGC)= area $(ANGM)$.

9*. Suppose that AB, CD are two parallel straight lines, E the midpoint of CD, and F, G the respective points of intersection of AC, BE and of AE, BD. Prove that FG is parallel to AB.

10. Through the vertex C of parallelogram $ABCD$ a straight line is drawn meeting AB, AD in P, Q respectively. Prove that $(BP)(DQ)$ is constant.

11*. Let A be one corner of a parallelogram $ABCD$. A straight line through A meets the diagonal BD at P and the sides BC, CD at Q, R respectively. Prove that $AP^2 = (PQ)(PR)$.

12. Given triangle ABC, points P, Q, R are taken on BC, CA, AB so that

$$BP : PC = CQ : QA = AR : RB = m : n.$$

Prove that

$$\text{area}(PQR) : \text{area}(ABC) = m^3 + n^3 : (m + n)^3.$$

13. $ABCD$ is a quadrilateral. The line through A parallel to DC meets BD at E and the line through D parallel to AB meets AC at F. Prove that EF is parallel to BC.

2.5   Elementary trigonometry

Trigonometry is an essential tool in Geometry. As we observed above, its proper place in the development of the subject follows the study of similar triangles. The basic formulae, and those which are used most often, should be *learned*. One cannot *use* a formula *flexibly,* or recognise situations where it may be relevant, if one does not know exactly what it says without looking it up first. One also needs lots of *practice* to master the variety of necessary techniques. Though we are ultimately interested in using trigonometry to help solve problems in geometry, there are no such applications in this particular section. Instead the section is devoted to giving the necessary training in the important art of handling trigonometric functions fluently.

We assume that you already know the basic definition of the six trigonometrical ratios – sin, cos, tan, cosec, sec, cot and that, following our comments in §2.3, you now understand that these are functions of angles and do not depend either on the particular *triangles* to which the are applied, or on the *units* being used to measure these angles. This is important when one denotes angles by *numbers* (as every calculator knows). We adopt the strict convention that, when an angle is denoted by a *pure* number (with no mention of units) it refers to the size of the angle *in radians*; when we wish to denote an angle by its size *in degrees* we will always include the degrees symbol "*o*". (We remind you that a straight angle has size π radians and size 180° in degrees.) When you study calculus it should become clear that *radian* measure is the natural measure for angles. But in Geometry and Trigonometry there is nothing to stop us using degrees, and it is often convenient to do so; nevertheless, it will still sometimes be more natural to use radians (for example, $\frac{\pi}{7}$ is both more suggestive and simpler than $(25\frac{5}{7})^o$).

We begin with a list of formulae you should learn by heart, if they are not already known.

(1) $\sin^2 A + \cos^2 A = 1.$ (A version of Pythagoras's theorem)
(2) $\sec^2 A = 1 + \tan^2 A.$ (Divide (1) by $\cos^2 A$.)
(3) $\operatorname{cosec}^2 A = 1 + \cot^2 A.$ (Divide (1) by $\sin^2 A$.)

Given an angle A (in degrees), $180^\circ - A$ is the *supplement* of A, and $90^\circ - A$ is the *complement* of A.

(4) $\sin(90^\circ - A) = \cos A;$ $\cos(90^\circ - A) = \sin A$
          and $\tan(90^\circ - A) = \cot A.$
(5) $\sin(180^\circ - A) = \sin A;$ $\cos(180^\circ - A) = -\cos A$
          and $\tan(180^\circ - A) = -\tan A.$
(6) $\sin(-A) = -\sin A;$ $\cos(-A) = \cos A;$
          and $\tan(-A) = -\tan A.$

Formulae involving two angles and multiple angles

(7) $\sin(A + B) = \sin A \cos B + \cos A \sin B$ (The proof - for acute angles $(x + y)$ only - is given by the diagram below, where $OC = 1$, $DC = \sin(x + y)$, $OF = \cos y$, $EF = \sin x \cos y$, $FC = \sin y$, $GC = \sin y \cos x$, $DC = DG + GC = EF + GC$, that is $\sin(x + y) = \sin x \cos y + \cos x \sin y$.

(8) $\sin(A - B) = \sin A \cos B - \cos A \sin B.$
     Put $-B$ for B in (7); then use (6).

(9) $\cos(A + B) = \cos A \cos B - \sin A \sin B.$
     Put $90^\circ - A$ for A in (8); then use (4).

(10) $\cos(A - B) = \cos A \cos B + \sin A \sin B.$ *Put $-B$ for B in (9); then use (6).*

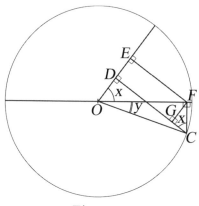

Figure 1

(11) $\tan(A+B) = (\tan A + \tan B)/(1 - \tan A \tan B)$. *(7) ÷ (9).*

(12) $\tan(A-B) = (\tan A - \tan B)/(1 + \tan A \tan B)$. *(8) ÷ (10).*

(13) $\sin 2A = 2 \sin A \cos A$. *Put $B = A$ in (7).*

(14) $\cos 2A = \cos^2 A - \sin^2 A$ *Put $B = A$ in (7).*
       $= 2\cos^2 A - 1 = 1 - 2\sin^2 A$. *Use (1).*

(15) $\cos^2 A = \frac{1}{2}(1 + \cos 2A)$. *Rearrangement of (14).*
       $\sin^2 A = \frac{1}{2}(1 - \cos 2A)$. *Rearrangement of (14).*

(16) If $t = \tan(A/2)$, then

$$
\begin{aligned}
\sin A &= 2t/(1+t^2), \\
\cos A &= (1-t^2)/(1+t^2) \text{ and} \\
\tan A &= 2t/(1-t^2).
\end{aligned}
$$

Put $\frac{A}{2}$ for A, B in (11); then use (2).

Exercise 2(d)

14*. Prove that

(i) $\cos A = 1/\left(1 + \tan A \tan \frac{A}{2}\right)$.

(ii) $\tan\left(45° + \frac{A}{2}\right) = (1 + \sin A)/\cos A = \cos A/(1 - \sin A)$.

15*. Prove that

(i) $\sin 3A = 3\sin A - 4\sin^3 A$;

(ii) $\cos 3A = 4\cos^3 A - 3\cos A$.

16*. Prove that

(i)

$$\begin{aligned} \sin(A + B)\sin(A - B) &= \sin^2 A - \sin^2 B \\ &= \cos^2 B - \cos^2 A \end{aligned}$$

and

(ii)

$$\begin{aligned} \cos(A + B)\cos(A - B) &= \cos^2 A - \sin^2 B \\ &= \cos^2 B - \sin^2 A. \end{aligned}$$

17*. Prove that $\sin\frac{A}{2} + \cos\frac{A}{2} = \pm\sqrt{(1 + \sin A)}$.

Factor Formulae

(17)

$$\sin P + \sin Q = 2\sin\frac{P + Q}{2}\cos\frac{P - Q}{2}$$

(7) +(8) with $A = \frac{P+Q}{2}, B = \frac{P-Q}{2}$.

(18)

$$\sin P - \sin Q = 2\cos\frac{P + Q}{2}\sin\frac{P - Q}{2}.$$

(7)   (8) with $A = \frac{P+Q}{2}, B = \frac{P-Q}{2}$.

(19)
$$\cos P + \cos Q = 2 \cos \frac{P+Q}{2} \cos \frac{P-Q}{2}.$$

(9) +(10) with $A = \frac{P+Q}{2}, B = \frac{P-Q}{2}$.

(20)
$$\cos P - \cos Q = -2 \sin \frac{P+Q}{2} \sin \frac{P-Q}{2}.$$

(9) − (10) with $A = \frac{P+Q}{2}, B = \frac{P-Q}{2}$.

Exercise 2(e)

18. Prove that $\sin(A+B+C) = \sin A \cos B \cos C + \sin B \cos C \cos A + \sin C \cos A \cos B - \sin A \sin B \sin C$.

19*. Prove that $\tan(A + B + C) =$

$$\frac{\tan A + \tan B + \tan C - \tan A \tan B \tan C}{1 - \tan B \tan C - \tan C \tan A - \tan A \tan B}.$$

Worked example

4. If $A + B + C = 180^o$, prove that

$$\cos A + \cos B - \cos C = 4 \cos \frac{A}{2} \cos \frac{B}{2} \sin \frac{C}{2} - 1.$$

Solution

$$
\begin{aligned}
\text{LHS} &= 2 \cos \tfrac{A+B}{2} \cos \tfrac{A-B}{2} + \cos(A+B) && \text{(by (19) \& (5))}\\
&= 2 \cos \tfrac{A+B}{2} \cos \tfrac{A-B}{2} + 2 \cos^2 \left(\tfrac{A+B}{2}\right) - 1 && \text{(by (14))}\\
&= 2 \sin \tfrac{C}{2} \left(\cos \tfrac{A-B}{2} + \cos \tfrac{A+B}{2}\right) - 1 && \text{(by (4))}\\
&= 4 \cos \tfrac{A}{2} \cos \tfrac{B}{2} \sin \tfrac{C}{2} - 1 = \text{RHS}. && \text{(by (19))}
\end{aligned}
$$

■

Whenever you are trying to prove an identity like this one your final solution should *never* start with the identity and manipulate it as if it were an equation. If that is how you happen to have worked *in rough*, the working must be reorganised to provide a logical proof. A logical proof should always start with one side - as in the above example - and show that it is equal to the other side, justifying each step in terms of known facts. (It is often wise to start with what looks like the *most awkward* side and try to simplify it to get the other side.)

Exercise 2(f)

Identities like the one in the above worked example are often needed to establish geometrical *inequalities*, where A, B, C are the angles of a triangle.

20*. If $A + B + C = 180^{\circ}$, prove that

$$\cos A + \cos B + \cos C = 4 \sin \frac{A}{2} \sin \frac{B}{2} \sin \frac{C}{2} + 1.$$

21*. If $A + B + C = 180^{\circ}$, prove that

$$\sin A + \sin B + \sin C = 4 \cos \frac{A}{2} \cos \frac{B}{2} \cos \frac{C}{2}.$$

22*. If $A + B + C = 180^{\circ}$, prove that

$$\tan A + \tan B + \tan C = \tan A \tan B \tan C.$$

23*. If $A + B + C = 180^{\circ}$, prove that

$$\cot \frac{A}{2} + \cot \frac{B}{2} + \cot \frac{C}{2} = \cot \frac{A}{2} \cot \frac{B}{2} \cot \frac{C}{2}.$$

24. If $A + B + C = 180°$, prove that

    (i) $\sin 2A + \sin 2B + \sin 2C = 4 \sin A \sin B \sin C$;

    (ii) $\cos 2A + \cos 2B + \cos 2C = -4 \cos A \cos B \cos C - 1$.

25*. Prove that $\tan 15° = 2 - \sqrt{3}$.

26*. Prove that $\sin 18° = (\sqrt{5} - 1)/4$.

27. Prove that $\sin 54° - \sin 18° = \frac{1}{2}$.

28*. Prove that for any positive integer n,

$$\tan n\theta = \frac{\binom{n}{1} \tan \theta - \binom{n}{3} \tan \theta + \binom{n}{5} \tan^5 \theta - \dots}{\binom{n}{0} - \binom{n}{2} \tan^2 \theta + \binom{n}{4} \tan^4 \theta - \dots}$$

29*. Prove that $\tan(4\theta - \phi) = 1$, where $\tan \theta = 1/5$ and $\tan \phi = 1/239$.

30*. Prove that

$$\sin A + \sin(A + B) + \sin(A + 2B) + \dots + \sin(A + 10B)$$

$$= \frac{\sin(A + 5B) \sin \left(\frac{11B}{2} \right)}{\sin(B/2)}.$$

31. Factorise the following polynomial completely as a product of polynomials of smaller degree with real coefficients:

$$x^8 - 2x^4 y^4 \cos 4\theta + y^8.$$

32*. Prove that $\sin \dfrac{\pi}{7} \sin \dfrac{2\pi}{7} \sin \dfrac{3\pi}{7} \sin \dfrac{4\pi}{7} \sin \dfrac{5\pi}{7} \sin \dfrac{6\pi}{7} \sin \dfrac{7\pi}{7} = \dfrac{7}{64}$.

33. Prove that

    (i) $\operatorname{cosec} 2A + \cot 2A = \cot A$;

(ii) $\cos A = \cos^4\left(\frac{A}{2}\right) - \sin^4\left(\frac{A}{2}\right)$;

(iii) $\tan A + \sec A = \tan\left(\frac{\pi}{4} + \frac{A}{2}\right)$;

(iv) $\sec^2 A \,\operatorname{cosec}^2 A = \sec^2 A + \operatorname{cosec}^2 A$.

Is it true that, if a and b are positive real numbers satisfying $ab = a + b$, then there exists an angle A such that $a = \sec^2 A$ and $b = \operatorname{cosec}^2 A$?

34*. Prove that

(i) $\tan 50^\circ + \tan 60^\circ + \tan 70^\circ = \tan 80^\circ$;

(ii) $\tan 10^\circ + \tan 70^\circ = \tan 50^\circ + \tan 60^\circ$.

Worked example

5. Given that $\cos\alpha + \cos\beta = 1$, prove that

$$\frac{\cos\beta\cos(\alpha/2)}{\cos(\beta - \alpha/2)} + \frac{\cos\alpha\cos(\beta/2)}{\cos(\alpha - \beta/2)} = 1.$$

Solution

One approach is to put $s = \tan(\alpha/2)$ and $t = \tan(\beta/2)$. One can then show that "$\cos\alpha + \cos\beta = 1 \Leftrightarrow 1 - s^2 - t^2 - 3s^2t^2 = 0$". With a lot of additional tedious algebra one can then show that:

$$\frac{\cos\beta\cos(\alpha/2)}{\cos(\beta - \alpha/2)} + \frac{\cos\alpha\cos(\beta/2)}{\cos(\alpha - \beta/2)} - 1 = \frac{1 - s^2 - t^2 - 3s^2t^2}{(1 - t^2 + 2ts)(1 - s^2 + 2ts)}.$$

A different approach is to use $\cos\beta = 1 - \cos\alpha = 2\sin^2(\alpha/2)$ to show:

$$\frac{\cos\beta\cos(\alpha/2)}{\cos(\beta - \alpha/2)} = \frac{2\sin^2(\alpha/2)\cos(\alpha/2)}{2\sin^2\left(\frac{\alpha}{2}\right)\cos\frac{\alpha}{2} + \sin\beta\sin\frac{\alpha}{2}} = \frac{\sin\alpha}{\sin\alpha + \sin\beta}.$$

Similarly

$$\frac{\cos \alpha \cos(\beta/2)}{\cos(\alpha - \beta/2)} = \frac{2 \sin^2(\beta/2) \cos(\beta/2)}{2 \sin^2 \left(\frac{\beta}{2}\right) \cos \frac{\beta}{2} + \sin \alpha \sin \frac{\beta}{2}} = \frac{\sin \beta}{\sin \beta + \sin \alpha},$$

and the result follows. ∎

There are often many different ways to tackle an exercise. It pays to think, sometimes for quite a long time, before selecting and then ploughing ahead with your chosen method.

Exercise 2(g)

35. Solve the equation $\sin(80° - \theta) = 2 \cos 40° \sin \theta$, $0° < \theta < 90°$.

36*. If $\alpha, \beta, \gamma, \delta$ are the four roots of the equation

$$\sin 2\theta - m \cos \theta - n \sin \theta + r = 0,$$

prove that

    (i) $\alpha + \beta + \gamma + \delta = (2p + 1)\pi$ for some $p \in \mathbb{Z}$ (the integers);

    (ii) $\sin \alpha + \sin \beta + \sin \gamma + \sin \delta = m$;

    (iii) $\cos \alpha + \cos \beta + \cos \gamma + \cos \delta = n$;

    (iv) $\sin 2\alpha + \sin 2\beta + \sin 2\gamma + \sin 2\delta = 2mn - 4r$;

    (v) $\cos 2\alpha + \cos 2\beta + \cos 2\gamma + \cos 2\delta = n^2 - m^2$.

37. If α, β, γ are unequal and lie between 0 and 2π, and if

$$\cos \alpha + \cos \beta + \cos \gamma = \sin \alpha + \sin \beta + \sin \gamma = 0,$$

prove that

(i) $\cos^2 \alpha + \cos^2 \beta + \cos^2 \gamma = \sin^2 \alpha + \sin^2 \beta + \sin^2 \gamma = 3/2$;

(ii) $\cos 2\alpha + \cos 2\beta + \cos 2\gamma = \sin 2\alpha + \sin 2\beta + \sin 2\gamma = 0$.

38. Prove that

$$\left(\frac{\frac{1}{\cos 0^\circ \cos 15^\circ} + \frac{1}{\cos 15^\circ \cos 30^\circ} + \frac{1}{\cos 30^\circ \cos 45^\circ}}{+ \frac{1}{\cos 45^\circ \cos 60^\circ} + \frac{1}{\cos 60^\circ \cos 75^\circ}} \right) = \frac{\cos 15^\circ}{\sin^2 15^\circ}.$$

This looks like a result which should generalise. Investigate.

2.6   Sine and cosine rules

We conclude this chapter with some fundamental applications of trigonometry to the triangle. We use the standard notation for the sides of triangle ABC; namely $BC = a$, $CA = b$, $AB = c$, and angles $\widehat{A}, \widehat{B}, \widehat{C}$ (or sometimes just A, B, C) to denote $\angle CAB$, $\angle ABC$, $\angle BCA$ when appropriate. There is a variety of notation in common use for the area of triangle ABC. We may write $\triangle(ABC)$ or just $\triangle$ for the area, or write $[ABC]$ as we do in Chapter 3-7. The standard notation for the semi-perimeter of a triangle is $s = (a + b + c)/2$. The letters L, M, N are used consistently to denote the midpoints of the sides BC, CA, AB.

We write G to denote the *centroid*, O the *circumcentre*, and I the *incentre* of the triangle. We proved above that the three *medians* AL, BM, CN are concurrent at the *centroid* G. We assume you know that the three perpendicular bisectors of the sides BC, CA, AB are concurrent at the circumcentre O. (Make sure that you can reconstruct the proof : Exercise 1(f) 28.) We also assume you know that the bisectors of the three angles A, B, C are concurrent at the *incentre* I. (Make sure you can reconstruct the proof. First prove that if P lies on the bisector of $\angle CAB$, and X, Y are the feet of the perpendiculars from P to AC, AB then $PX = PY$; hence P is equidistant from the line AC and from the line AB. Now use this to complete the proof.) The letters R, r respectively denote the radii of the circumcircle and incircle of the triangle ABC.

We now deduce the Sine Rule.

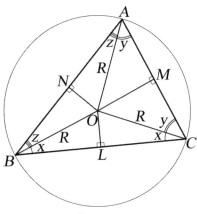

Figure 1

Using the notation in the diagram:

(i) Complete the equations :$(x + y + z) = \_\_\_^o$; $y + z = \_\_\_$.

(ii) Solve these to obtain $x = 90^o - \widehat{A}$.

(iii) Hence show $\angle BOL = \widehat{A}$.

(iv) Deduce that $a = BC = 2R \sin \widehat{A}$.

(v) Explain why it now follows that

$$\frac{a}{\sin \widehat{A}} = \frac{b}{\sin \widehat{B}} = \frac{c}{\sin \widehat{C}} = 2R.$$

This is known as the **SINE RULE**.

The main use of the Sine Rule is in the "solution of triangles".

(1) If $\widehat{A}, \widehat{B}, \widehat{C}$ and any one of a, b, c, R are known, then the remaining three can be calculated.

(2) If $a, b, \widehat{A}$ are known, then $\sin \widehat{B}$ can be calculated; there are then two possible values for $\widehat{B}$ (one, say β, between 0° and 90°, and also $180^o - \beta$). This is why there can be no "SSA" congruence "theorem"!

The Sine Rule allows us to reinterpret the usual "half base times height" formula for the area of a triangle as follows:

$$\triangle = \frac{1}{2}\text{base}\times\text{height} = \frac{1}{2}ab \sin \widehat{C} = \frac{1}{2}bc \sin \widehat{A} = \frac{1}{2}ca \sin \hat{B} = abc/4R.$$

We now prove the Cosine Rule.

Let ABC be a given triangle and let D be the foot of the perpendicular from A to BC. Then by Pythagoras's theorem for triangle ABD we have

Figure 2

$$c^2 = (a - b \cos \widehat{C})^2 + (b \sin \widehat{C})^2.$$

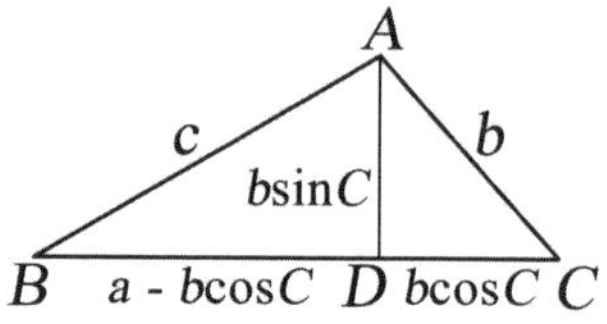

Moreover, if $\widehat{C} > 90^\circ$, then $\cos \widehat{C}$ is negative and the equation is still valid. Thus

$$c^2 = a^2 + b^2 - 2ab \cos \widehat{C}. \qquad \textbf{COSINE RULE}$$

Similarly $a^2 = b^2 + c^2 - 2bc \cos \widehat{A}$ and $b^2 = c^2 + a^2 - 2ca \cos \widehat{B}$. The main use of the Cosine Rule is in the "solution of triangles".

(1) If a, b, c are known, then $\widehat{A}, \widehat{B}, \widehat{C}$ may be calculated.

(2) If $a, b, \widehat{C}$ are known, then c may be calculated.

(1) corresponds to the SSS congruence theorem; (2) corresponds to the SAS congruence axiom.

Exercise 2(h)

39. Calculate $\sin \widehat{A}, \sin \widehat{B}, \sin \widehat{C}, \cos \widehat{A}, \cos \widehat{B}, \cos \widehat{C}, R$ when $a = 10, b = 17, c = 21$. What is the value of $\triangle$?

40*. Use $\triangle = \frac{1}{2}ab \sin \widehat{C}$ and $c^2 = a^2 + b^2 - 2ab \cos \widehat{C}$ to establish

$$\triangle = \sqrt{s(s-a)(s-b)(s-c)}. \qquad \textbf{HERON'S FORMULA}$$

41. Prove that if the bisector of $\widehat{A}$ meets BC at U, then

$$BU : UC = BA : AC.$$

42. Let ABC be a triangle with $\angle C = 60^o$. If the bisectors of $\angle CAB$ and $\angle ABC$ meet the opposite sides at P, Q, prove that $AB = AQ + BP$.

43*. Prove that the length of the bisector AU from A to BC is given by
$$AU^2 = \frac{bc(b+c+a)(b+c-a)}{(b+c)^2}.$$
Show that
$$AU \leq \frac{1}{2}(AB + BC).$$

Next we prove Apollonius's theorem.

Apollonius's theorem In the triangle ABC, let L be the midpoint of BC, and let $AL = l$. Then

$$l^2 = \frac{1}{4}(2b^2 + 2c^2 - a^2).$$

Proof

We have

$$\frac{1}{4}a^2 + l^2 - al\cos\theta,$$

$$b^2 = \frac{1}{4}a^2 + l^2 + al\cos\theta$$

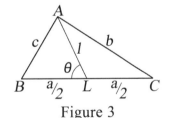

Figure 3

by applying the Cosine Rule to triangles ALB and ALC. Adding these we get the required result.

Note that adding the three forms of Apollonius's theorem for AL, BM, CN gives

$$4(l^2 + m^2 + n^2) = 3(a^2 + b^2 + c^2).$$

Exercise 2(i)

44. Prove that $AG = BC$ if and only if $\angle BGC = \pi/2$. If in addition $AB = AC$, calculate $\widehat{A}$.

45*. Let $AL = l$ and $AU = u$ (where L is the midpoint of BC and U is the point where the bisector of $\angle CAB$ meets BC). Prove that
$$\frac{l}{u} \geq \frac{(b+c)^2}{4bc},$$
with equality if and only if $b = c$.

46*. If $c = b + \frac{1}{2}a$ and P is a point of BC such that $BP : PC = 1 : 3$, prove that $\angle ACP = 2\angle APC$.

47. In triangle ABC the points D, U, L on BC are respectively the foot of the perpendicular from A onto BC, the point where the internal bisector of angle A meets BC, and the midpoint of BC. If the angles $\angle BAD, \angle DAU, \angle UAL, \angle LAC$ are all equal, determine the angles of the triangle ABC.

48. The convex pentagon $ABCDE$ has a circumcircle (i.e. A, B, C, D, E all lie on a single circle). The perpendicular distances of A from BC, CD, DE are p, q, s respectively. Determine (as a function of p, q, s) the perpendicular distance from A to the diagonal BE.

49*. Let $ABCD$ be a convex quadrilateral. Prove that if g is the greatest and h is the least of the distances AB, AC, AD, BC, BD, CD, then $g \geq h\sqrt{2}$.

2.7 Hints to starred problems, and answers to other selected problems

3. Consider DB. Similar if $AB : A'B' = BC : B'C'$
   $= CD : C'D' = DA : D'A'$ and $\angle DAB = \angle D'A'B'$.

6. This involves two applications of Theorem 4.

7. This has been included as a warning – like Worked Example 2; for although it looks like a ratio question, it in fact only involves areas.

9. The first step is to prove that triangles ABG and EDG are similar; then $AB/ED = AB/CE$, etc.

11. There are lots of pairs of similar triangles here. Try for example, APD and QPB; and ABQ and RCQ. You should expect to have to use at some stage $AD = BC$ or $AB = DC$.

14. Use (16).

15. Put $B = 2A$ in (7) and (9). Then use (13), (14) and tidy up.

17. Start from the square of both sides.

19. Use (11) twice.

20. If in doubt, read the worked example again.

21. $\sin C = 2 \sin \frac{A+B}{2} \cos \frac{A+B}{2}$.

22. Use the result of Exercise 18.

23. This is really a question about $A/2 + B/2 + C/2 = 90^o$.

25. Use tan $30^o = 1/\sqrt{3}$ and (16).

26. Prove that $\cos 5A = \cos A(1 - 12\sin^2 A + 16\sin^4 A)$; then consider $A = 18°$. (Alternatively, use a 72°-72°-36° triangle.)

28. Use induction (or de Moivre's theorem:

$$(\cos\theta + i\sin\theta)^n = \cos n\theta + i\sin n\theta.)$$

29. Work out $\tan 4\theta$ using Exercise 27; then use (12).

30. Multiply by $\sin\frac{B}{2}$. Then concentrate on the LHS using (20); it vanishes for $B = k360°/11$, where k is any positive integer, $1 \le k \le 10$.

31. $(x^2 - 2xy\cos\theta + y^2)(x^2 + 2xy\sin\theta + y^2)(x^2 + 2xy\cos\theta + y^2) \times (x^2 - 2xy\sin\theta + y^2)$.

32. Find $\sin 7\theta$ as a polynomial in terms of $\sin\theta$; then look at the equation $\sin 7\theta/\sin\theta = 0$ $(\theta \neq n\pi)$.

33. Yes. $a = b/(b-1) > 1$, and $1 < \sec^2 A < \infty$.

34. Work in terms of $\sqrt{3} = \tan 60°$. You will also need $\tan 10° = t$ and $\tan 30° = \tan(3 \times 10°)$.

35. $\theta = 30°$.

36. For parts (i), (ii) and (iii) form the equations satisfied by (i) $t = \tan(\theta/2)$, (ii) $s = \sin\theta$, (iii) $c = \cos\theta$; then use properties for roots of equations. You will need the formula for $\tan\left(\frac{\alpha}{2} + \frac{\beta}{2} + \frac{\gamma}{2} + \frac{\delta}{2}\right)$.

38. Yes, it does generalise! But how? Can your prove the generalisation?

39. $\sin\widehat{A} = 8/17, \sin\widehat{B} = 4/5, \sin\widehat{C} = 84/85, R = 85/8; \triangle = 84$.

40. $\sin^2 \widehat{C} + \cos^2 \widehat{C} = 1$ gives $16\triangle^2 = 4a^2b^2 - (a^2 + b^2 - c^2)^2$. Now factorise - do not multiply out.

41. Use the sine rule on triangles ABU and ACU. Remember that $\sin(180^\circ - \phi) = \sin\phi$ for the two angles at U.

43. Use the cosine rule for both triangles ABU and ACU and eliminate $\cos\theta$, where $\theta = \angle AUB$. You also have to use the result of Exercise 41.

44. $\widehat{A} = \arccos(4/5)$.

45. Use Apollonius's theorem, the result of Exercise 43, and prove that

$$16l^2b^2c^2 - (b + c)^4 u^2 = bc(b - c)^2(a - b + c)(a + b - c).$$

46. Use the cosine rule on triangles APB and APC, and the sine rule on triangle APC.

47. $\angle A = 90^\circ, \angle B = 67.5^\circ, \angle C = 22.5^\circ$

48. By expressing the area of triangle ABC in two ways prove that $p = (AB)(AC)/2R$. The answer is ps/q.

49. Why is it possible, without loss of generality, to take $\angle A \geq 90^\circ$, and $DA \geq AB$?

The imparting of factual knowledge is for us a secondary consideration. Above all we aim to promote in the reader a correct attitude, a certain discipline of thought, which would appear to be of even more essential importance in mathematics than in other scientific disciplines.
G.Polya & G. Szegö

The first rule of intelligent tinkering is to save all the parts.
P. Ehrlich

Only those topics which have a quality of "play" have educational value, and of all such games, Euclidean Geometry, with its constant references to underlying intuitively understood fundamentals, is the richest in meaning.
René Thom

Experience is the name everyone gives to their mistakes.
Oscar Wilde

Chapter 3

Circles

3.1   Unit 1: Elementary circle theorems

Definition of a circle

A circle is the locus of a point P that moves at a constant distance from a given point O. The point O is called the **centre** of the circle.

From the definition it can be seen that what we call a circle is often called the **circumference** of the circle. The word circumference is in fact used in this booklet when attention is being drawn to the fact that a point lies on the circle itself and does **not** lie in its interior.

Some authors use the word **disc** for the interior of a circle. If the disc does not contain the circumference it is called an **open disc**. If it does contain the circumference it is called a **closed disc**.

Many equivalent definitions of a circle are possible. Any property of a point P that holds if and only if P lies on a circle may be taken over as the definition of a circle; but the definition given here is the one that is directly related to the construction of a circle with a pair of compasses, so in a certain sense it is more basic than other possible definitions.

Radius and diameter

A straight line from the centre O to a point P on a circle is called a **radius**, and the same word is also used for the length OP.

If a straight line through O intersects a circle in distinct points A and B, then the line segment AB is called a **diameter** of the circle, and again the same word is used for the length AB. Obviously the diameter is twice the radius.

Angle

In some geometrical problems it is revealing to give the measure of an angle a sign, an angle in an anticlockwise sense being positive, and one in a clockwise sense being negative. Thus in Figure 1 $\angle AOB$ is positive and $\angle BOA$ has the same magnitude but as a signed angle is negative. But in most geometrical problems there is no need to make a distinction. The context almost always enables one to see whether the sign convention is being used. In proving the circle theorems in the next few pages the sign convention is used.

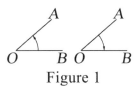

Figure 1

Theorem 1 (Angle in a semi-circle)

If AB is the diameter of a circle and P is a point on the circle, other than A or B, then $\angle APB = 90^\circ \pmod{180^\circ}$.

Note that in Figure 2 the signed $\angle APB = 90^\circ$ but if P had been in the lower semicircle, then the signed $\angle APB$ would have been -90°

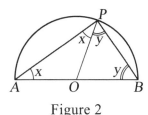

Figure 2

Proof

Notice that $OA = OP$ (both radii), so $\angle OAP = \angle APO = x$, since triangle OAP is isosceles. Similarly $\angle OPB = \angle PBO = y$. Hence $\angle APB = x + y = 90^\circ$, being half the angle sum of triangle APB. ∎

Exercise

1. Prove the converse of Theorem 1, that if A and B are two distinct fixed points and P moves so that $\angle APB = 90^\circ$ (mod

180°), then the locus of P is a circle on AB as diameter (excluding the points A and B).

Arc, chord, segment, sector.

The part of a circle between two distinct points A and B lying on it is called the **arc** AB. For each pair of points there are two arcs, one going from A to B anticlockwise, the other going clockwise. Unless the straight line AB is a diameter these two arcs are of different length; then the longer is called the **major arc** and the shorter the **minor arc**. The straight line segment AB is called the **chord** AB. If one specifies one of the arcs AB then the part of the disc bounded by the arc and the chord is called a **segment**. A chord divides a disc into two segments, and the second segment is often referred to as the **alternate segment** (alternate here meaning other). The part of the disc bounded by the arc AB and the radii OA and OB is called the **sector** OAB. As with a segment one has to know which of the two arcs AB is being referred to. Now $\angle AOB$ is often referred to as the angle **subtended** at the centre of the circle by the arc AB. Likewise if P is a point on the circle distinct from A and B then $\angle APB$ is often referred to as the angle **subtended** at P by the arc AB.

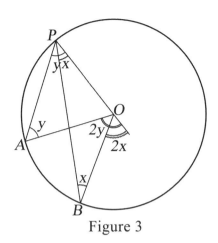

Figure 3

Theorem 2 (Angle subtended at the centre by an arc = 2× angle subtended at the circumference.)

Let AB be a fixed arc on a circle, centre O; and let P be a point on the circumference in the alternate segment (that is not lying on the designated arc). Then $\angle AOB = 2 \times \angle APB$.

Proof

In Figure 3 the case is shown in which PO does not intersect the arc AB. The proof when PO does intersect the arc AB is slightly different and contains a plus sign rather than a minus sign. A full proof should contain an analysis of both cases. (It is often the case that a proof in Geometry needs to be broken down into several cases corresponding to a variety of different possible figures.)

Observe that $OA = OP$ (both radii), so $\angle OAP = \angle APO = y$, since triangle OAP is isosceles. It follows that $\angle AOQ = 2y$ (exterior angle of a triangle equal to the sum of the two interior angles). Similarly if $\angle BPO = x$, then $\angle BOQ = 2x$. Then $\angle AOB = 2y - 2x = 2(y - x) = 2 \times \angle APB$. ■

Corollary (Angles in the same segment are equal.)

If P_1 and P_2 are two distinct points of the circumference in the alternate segment of an arc AB then $\angle AP_1B = \angle AP_2B$. This is immediate from Theorem 2, both angles being equal to $\frac{1}{2} \times \angle AOB$. This result is illustrated in Figure 4.

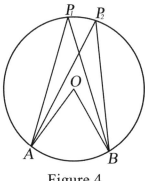

Figure 4

Cyclic quadrilateral, convex quadrilateral.

A quadrilateral is **cyclic** if and only if its four vertices lie on a circle. It is a convention that if one refers to a cyclic quadrilateral $ABCD$ then the vertices A, B, C, D lie in that order around the circle. By Theorem 2 each of the angles $\angle ABC, \angle BCD, \angle CDA, \angle DAB$ must be less than 180°, and as this may be taken to be the definition of a **convex** quadrilateral it follows that every cyclic quadrilateral is convex.

Theorem 3 (The opposite angles of a cyclic quadrilateral add up to 180°.)

If $APBQ$ is a cyclic quadrilateral then $\angle APB + \angle BQA = 180^o$.

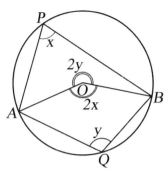

Figure 5

The proof consists of two applications of Theorem 2, see Figure 5. Note that $2x + 2y = 360^o$, so $x + y = 180^o$.

In connection with Figure 5, note that the $\angle AQB = -\angle BQA = -y = x - 180^o = x \pmod{180^o}$. This means that when one uses signed angles the corollary to Theorem 2 may be extended to read:

if P_1 and P_2 are two distinct points on the circumference of a circle and AB is an arc (A and B both being distinct from P_1 and P_2), then $\angle AP_1B = \angle AP_2B \pmod{180^o}$. ■

Exercise

2. If A, B, C are three distinct non-collinear points then a circle may be drawn through A, B and C.

This circle is called the **circumcircle** of triangle ABC. It is important to realize that a circle may always be drawn through three non-collinear points, but that conditions are required before one can assert that four points lie on a circle. For conditions of this type to be significant they must be necessary **and** sufficient, so attention must next be given to establishing the converse of both the corollary to Theorem 2 and Theorem 3.

Theorem 4 (Converse of the corollary to Theorem 2)

If A, B are fixed points and P_1 and P_2 lie on the same side of the straight line AB and satisfy $\angle AP_1B = \angle AP_2B$, then P_2 lies on the circumcircle of triangle AP_1B.

Proof

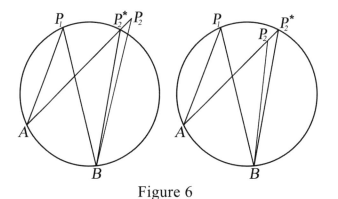

Figure 6

Suppose not. In this event P_2 either lies outside the circumcircle of AP_1B (Figure 6, left hand figure) or lies inside the circumcircle (Figure 6, right-hand figure). Let AP_2 meet the circumcircle at P_2^*. Join BP_2^*. Then $\angle AP_1B = \angle AP_2^*B$ (corollary to Theorem 2). But $\angle AP_1B = \angle AP_2B$. Hence $\angle AP_2^*B = \angle AP_2B$. But in the left-hand figure $\angle AP_2^*B > \angle AP_2B$ and in the right-hand figure angle $AP_2^*B < \angle AP_2B$. These contradictions establish the result. ∎

Theorem 5 (Converse of Theorem 3)

If A, B are fixed points and P_1, P_2 lie on opposite sides of the straight line AB and satisfy $\angle AP_1B + \angle BP_2A = 180^o$, then P_2 lies on the circumcircle of triangle AP_1B.

Exercise

3. Prove Theorem 5.

Theorem 6 (Intersecting chord theorem)

Let AD and BC be two chords of a circle (possibly extended) and let X be their point of intersection, then

$$(CX)(BX) = (DX)(AX)$$

Proof

Two figures are possible according as X lies inside or outside the circle. These are Figures 7 and 8 below.

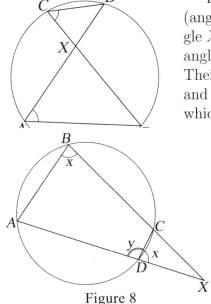

Figure 8

In Figure 7 we have $\angle BAD = \angle BCD$ (angles in the same segment). With angle X being common it follows that triangle BAX is similar to triangle DCX. Their sides are therefore in proportion and hence $CX/AX = DX/BX$ from which the result follows.

In Figure 8 $ABCD$ is a cyclic quadrilateral. It follows from Theorem 3 that $\angle ABC + \angle CDA = x + y = 180°$. It follows that triangle BAX is similar to triangle DCX and the result now follows as previously. ∎

Theorem 7 (Converse of intersecting chord theorem – internal crossing)

If DA and BC are two line segments which intersect internally at a point X such that

$$(CX)(BX) = (DX)(AX),$$

then $ABDC$ is a cyclic quadrilateral.

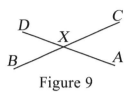

Figure 9

Proof

We have $CX/DX = AX/BX$ and $\angle CXA = \angle DXB$ (opposite angles). Hence by the side-angle-side version of similarity it follows that triangles CAX and DBX are similar. Hence $\angle ACX = \angle BDX$; that is $\angle ACB = \angle ADB$. It now follows from Theorem 4 that $ABDC$ is a cyclic quadrilateral. ∎

Exercises

4. Prove the converse of the intersecting chord theorem when the crossing is external.

5. The convex hexagon $ABCDEF$ is inscribed in a circle. Prove that the diagonals AD, BE, CF are concurrent if and only if

$$(AB)(CD)(EF) = (BC)(DE)(FA).$$

6. Let S be a circle centre O and Q be an internal point of S. Let AQC be a chord of S. If the radius of S is r, prove that

$$r^2 - OQ^2 = (AQ)(QC).$$

Now suppose that K is a point outside S and let KC meet S at B. Prove that

$$OK^2 - r^2 = (KB)(KC).$$

If S is a circle of radius r and centre O, and P is any point in the plane of S then the value of $OP^2 - r^2$ is called the **power** of P with respect to S. The definition shows the power of P is positive, zero or negative according as P is outside, on or inside S.

Exercises

7. Three points A, B, C lie on a given circle, centre O. Let P be the midpoint of the arc AB lying on the opposite side of AB to C. Let Q, R be the feet of the perpendiculars from P on to AC, BC respectively. Prove that

$$OQ^2 + OR^2 = 2OC^2.$$

8. From the point of intersection of the diagonals of a cyclic quadrilateral perpendiculars are drawn to the sides; prove that the sum of any two opposite angles of the quadrilateral formed by joining the feet of these perpendiculars is double one of the angles between the two diagonals.

9. A chord CD is drawn at right angles to a fixed diameter AB of a given circle and DP is any other chord meeting AB at Q. Prove that $\angle PCQ$ is bisected by CA.

10. Circles S_1, S_2 with centres O_1, O_2 and radii r_1, r_2 respectively, are drawn so the distance between their centres is given by

$$O_1O_2 = (r_1^2 + r_2^2)^{\frac{1}{2}}.$$

S_1 and S_2 intersect at A and B. From the point P on S_1 furthest from O_2 lines PA, PB are drawn to intersect S_2 at D, E respectively. Prove that DE is the diameter of S_2 perpendicular to O_1O_2. A point Q (distinct from P) is now chosen on the major arc AB of S_1. Now QA, QB are drawn to intersect S_2 at F, G respectively. Prove that FG is also a diameter of S_2. Locate, with proof, the point where FB and GA meet.

11. Two circles PAB, QAB intersect at A and B. It is given that PAQ is a straight line. Prove that as P and Q vary on their respective circles, BP/BQ is constant.

12. A, B, C, D, P are five points on a circle. Perpendiculars PK, PL, PM, PN are drawn to AB, BC, CD, DA respectively. Show that

$$(PK)(PM) = (PL)(PN).$$

13. $ABCDE$ is a regular pentagon and P is a point on its circumcircle between A and E. Show that

$$PA + PC + PE = PB + PD.$$

14. Two circles S_1 and S_2 intersect at A and B . The point R lies on S_2. RA, RB meet S_1 at P, Q respectively. Prove that, as R moves on S_2, PQ remains constant in length.

15. A, B are fixed points on a circle, not diametrically opposite each other. P is a variable point of the circle and Q is the point diametrically opposite to P. Find the locus of the point of intersection of AP and BQ.

16. Let $ABCD$ be a cyclic quadrilateral and suppose that AC and BD meet at the point X . Prove that

(arc $AB+$ arc DC) : (arc $BC+$arc DA) $= \angle AXB : \angle CXB.$

3.2 Unit 1: Hints and Solutions

1. Move a point O from B towards A until $OB = OP$. Say why this is always possible. Next prove that when O is in this position $OA = OP$ also. The locus is therefore a circle centre O (excluding A and B) on AB as diameter. Note this means when you have a right-angled triangle that the centre of the circumcircle of the triangle is at the midpoint of the hypotenuse.

2. AB and AC are not parallel so their perpendicular bisectors meet at a point O. O has the property that it is equidistant from A, B and C, so it is the centre of the circle through these points. There can only be one such circle.

3. Frame a proof by contradiction as in Theorem 4.

4. The proof is almost identical to that which was used in proving Theorem 7, except that $\angle CXA$ and $\angle DXB$ are in fact one and the same angle and Theorem 5 needs to be used rather than Theorem 4 in the final step to conclude that $ABCD$ is cyclic.

5. Suppose that the diagonals are concurrent at X, then triangles ABX and EDX are similar, and hence

$$AB/DE = BX/XD.$$

Now work out similar expressions for CD/FA and EF/BC and multiply the three equations together. If you have chosen the right-hand sides wisely, the result will evidently equal 1. For the converse let AD, BE meet at X and draw CX to meet the circle at G. Now prove $EF/EG = FA/GA$ and since $\angle EFA = \angle EGA$, triangles EFA and EGA are similar. This implies F and G coincide.

6. For the first part use Theorem 6 with the chord AQC and the diameter through Q as the two intersecting chords. For the second part use Theorem 6 with the chord KCB and the diameter which when extended passes through K as the two intersecting chords.

7. Explain why arc $AP =$ arc PB implies $\angle ACP = \angle PCB$. Now show triangles PQC and PRC are congruent and hence that $PQ = PR$. This, together with chord $AP =$ chord PB, means triangles AQP and BRP are also congruent. Now prove $(QA)(QC) = (BR)(RC)$ and use the results of Exercise 6.

8. Let the quadrilateral be $ABCD$. Suppose that AC and BD meet at X and let the feet of the perpendiculars on to AB, BC, CD, DA be K, L, M, N respectively.

$$\angle ANX + \angle AKX = 2 \times 90^o = 180^o$$

and hence, using Theorem 5, the figure $ANXK$ is a cyclic quadrilateral. Hence $\angle AKN = \angle AXN$. Similarly

$$\angle BKL = \angle BXL, \ \angle LMC = \angle LXC$$

and $\angle NMD = \angle NXD$. It now follows that

$$\angle NKL + \angle NML = 2 \times \angle AXB.$$

9. Suppose that CD meets AB at N and CQ meets the circle again at R. Prove that triangles QND and QNC are congruent and then use Theorem 6 to deduce $RQ = PQ$. Now prove triangles ARQ and APQ are congruent. It then follows that arc $AR =$ arc AP and hence $\angle ACR = \angle ACP$.

10. Let $\angle PAO_1 = x$, then $\angle O_1PA = x$, since triangle O_1PA is isosceles. Hence, by Theorem 2, $\angle AO_1O_2 = 2x$. Now $(O_1O_2)^2 = (O_1A)^2 + (O_2A)^2 = r_1^2 + r_2^2$ so $\angle O_1AO_2 = 90^o$. From which $\angle O_1O_2A = 90^o - 2x$. Furthermore

$$\angle DAO_2 = 90^o - x = \angle ADO_2.$$

It follows that $\angle DO_2A = 2x$ and so $\angle PO_2D = 90^o$. Similarly $\angle PO_2E = 90^o$ and DO_2E is a straight line. For the next part $\angle GBE = \angle PBQ = \angle PAQ = \angle DAF$. It follows that arc $DF = $ arc EG. Hence FG is also a diameter of S_2, being the image of DE under a rotation about O_2. For the last part let AG and FB meet at R. Since FG is a diameter of S_2 then $\angle GAF = \angle GBF = 90^o$ and hence $\angle QAR = \angle QBR = 90^o$. Hence R lies on S_1 at the opposite end of the diameter through Q.

11. Let P_1AQ_1 and P_2AQ_2 be two such lines. Then $\angle AP_1B = \angle AP_2B$ and $\angle AQ_1B = \angle AQ_2B$ (angles in the same segment). Hence triangles BP_1Q_1 and BP_2Q_2 are similar and the result follows. You should check that the result is still true when the order of the points on the line is APQ or AQP (rather than PAQ), though the reasoning is slightly more difficult.

12. Remember that a quadrilateral having a pair of opposite angles equal to 90° is cyclic. For example $PNAK$ is cyclic. Let $\angle PNK = x$. Then $x = \angle PAK = \angle PCL = \angle PML$, since both of the figures $ABCP$ and $PMCL$ are cyclic. Similarly $\angle NKP = \angle PLM$. Hence triangles PNK and PML are similar and the result follows.

13. Prove that $\angle EPD = 36^o$ and $\angle APE = 144^o$. Let $\angle PEA = x$. From here you can now show

$$\angle PDC = 72^o + x, \; \angle PCD = 72^o - x, \; \angle PAE = 36^o - x$$

and $\angle PCB = 36° + x$. The result now follows from establishing the identity

$$\sin x = \sin(36°+x) - \sin(36°-x) + \sin(72°-x) - \sin(72°+x)$$

and to prove this you require $\sin 18° = (\sqrt{5} - 1)/4$ and $\sin 54° = (\sqrt{5}+1)/4$.

14. Take two configurations labeled R_1, P_1, Q_1 and R_2, P_2, Q_2. Now

$$\angle P_1 A P_2 = \angle R_1 A R_2 = \angle R_1 B R_2 = \angle Q_1 B Q_2 = \angle Q_1 A Q_2.$$

Hence $\angle P_1 A Q_1 = \angle P_2 A Q_2$ which implies $P_1 Q_1 = P_2 Q_2$.

15. The locus is a circle through A and B. The proof is very similar to that used in Exercise 10 and is therefore not repeated.

16. $\angle AXB = \angle DBC + \angle ACB$ and $\angle CXB = \angle BDC + \angle ACD$. The result follows since an arc is proportional in length to the angle it subtends at any point on the circumference.

3.3 Unit 2: Tangency theorems and Ptolemy's theorem

Definition of a tangent

A line parallel to a given chord of a circle is perpendicular to the diameter of the circle through the midpoint of the chord. Such a line is **tangent** to the circle if it passes through an end point of the diameter and then it meets the circle in one point only.

Analytically, the equation of a circle is of the second degree and that of a line is of the first degree. The points of intersection of the circle and the line arise as the solution of these equations as a simultaneous pair. The method of substitution leads to a quadratic equation. This equation has either two real roots and then the line intersects the circle in a pair of distinct points, or it has coninci-dent roots and then the line is tangent to the circle or it has no real roots and then the line does not intersect the circle at all.

By definition if a line l is tangent to a circle at a point P then l is perpendicular to the radius OP.

Exercises

1. Prove that there are two tangents to a circle in any given direction.

2. Prove that there are two tangents to a circle through any point external to that circle.

Theorem 1 (Tangents from an external point are equal in length)

Let S be a circle centre O, and let T be an external point. If the tangents to S through T meet S at P and Q then (i) $TP = TQ$ and (ii) a circle may be drawn through O, P, T and Q the centre of which is the midpoint of OT.

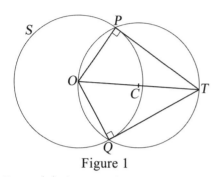

Figure 1

Proof

Pythagoras's theorem gives us part (i). Each of TP^2 and TQ^2 is equal to $TO^2 - r^2$, where r is the radius of S. Note the consequence that for an external point T, **the length of the tangent from T is the power of T with respect to S.**

Part (ii) follows from the fact that $\angle OPT = \angle OQT = 90^o$, so by Example 1 of Unit 1, both P and Q lie on the circle with diameter OT.   ∎

Theorem 2 (Alternate segment theorem)

Let TP be tangent to a circle at P and PQ a chord of that circle. Let R be a point on the circumference of the circle in the alternate segment to that cut off by PQ. Then

$$\angle TPQ = \angle PRQ.$$

Proof

$\angle PRQ$ is independent of the position of R (angles in the same segment are equal), so it is sufficient to prove the theorem when R is at the opposite end of the diameter through Q.

Then $\angle TPQ = 90^\circ - \angle QPO$ (tangent and radius at right angles)$= \angle OPR$ (angle in a semi-circle is a right angle). But triangle ORP is isosceles, so $\angle OPR = \angle ORP$ which is the same angle

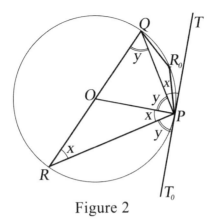

Figure 2

as $\angle PRQ$. This proof assumes $\angle TPQ$ is acute. If it is obtuse the theorem still holds. For from Figure 2 $\angle TPQ = \angle PRQ$ implies that $\angle QPT_0 = \angle QR_0P$, since both $\angle TPQ + \angle QPT_0$ and $\angle PRQ + \angle QR_0P$ equal $180°$. ■

The converse of the alternate segment theorem is just as important in geometrical applications as the theorem itself. There are in fact very few ways of proving a line is a tangent to a circle and the importance of the converse is that it provides one of those ways.

Theorem 3 (Converse of alternate segment theorem)

Let T, P, Q be three fixed points and suppose that the variable point R moves so that the directed $\angle PRQ = \angle TPQ$ (mod $180°$), then the locus of R is a circle through P and Q having PT tangent to it at P.

Proof

From Theorems 4 and 5 of Unit 1 we already know that if directed $\angle PQR = $ constant (mod 180°), then the locus of R is a circle passing through P and Q. Suppose that this circle is not tangent to PT at T then it must intersect it at a further point U on one side of P or the other. Since U is on the locus then, with reference to Figure 3, we have **either** $\angle PU_1Q = \angle TPQ$, which is false since $\angle PQU_1$ is not zero **or** $\angle PU_2Q = -\angle QU_2P = \angle TPQ - 180^o$, which is false since $\angle PQU_2$ is not zero. This contradiction shows that the locus of R does not intersect PT in a second point.

This means PT is tangent to the circle at P. ∎

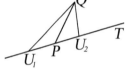

Figure 3

Theorem 4 (Tangent chord theorem)

Let T be an external point to a circle S and suppose that TAB is a chord intersecting S at A and B and TP is a tangent touching S at P, then

$$TP^2 = (TA)(TB).$$

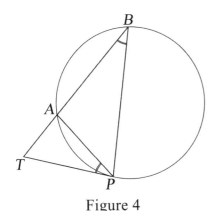

Figure 4

Proof

In triangles TPA and TBP we have (i) $\angle TPA = \angle PBA$ (alternate segment theorem) and (ii) $\angle PTB$ is common. Hence these triangles are similar and it follows that $TP : TB = TA : TP$, that is $TP^2 = (TA)(TB)$. ∎

Exercises

3. Prove the converse of Theorem 4, that if TAB and TP are two lines intersecting at T and $TP^2 = (TA)(TB)$, then the circle PAB touches TP at P.

4. Two circles S_1 and S_2 intersect at A. Through A any pair of straight lines BAC and B_0AC_0 are drawn with B, B_0 on S_1 and C, C_0 on S_2. Prove that the chord BB_0 of S_1 and C_0C of S_2 are inclined at a constant angle.

5. A circle is given with AB as diameter and P is another point on the circumference. M is the foot of the perpendicular from P on to AB. On AM, MB as diameters two circles are drawn meeting AP, BP at Q, R respectively. Prove that QR touches both circles.

6. Two circles with centres A and B intersect at right angles. Their common chord meets AB at F. DE is a chord of the first circle passing through B. Prove that A, D, E, F are concyclic.

7. Two circles S_1 and S_2 touch at A. The chord PK of S_1 touches S_2 at R. PA meets S_2 at T. RA meets S_1 at Q. Prove that PQ is parallel to RT.

8. Prove that a quadrilateral with successive sides of length a, b, c, d possesses an inscribed circle if and only if $a+c = b+d$.

9. A diameter AB of a circle is produced to any point C. The point of contact of a tangent from C to the circle is T. The perpendicular through C to AC meets the extension of AT at D. Prove that $CT = CD$.

10. From a fixed point A of a given circle are drawn two chords AP, AQ equally inclined to a fixed chord AT. Prove PQ is fixed in direction.

11. P, Q, R are three points on a circle. The tangents at Q and R meet at T. Perpendiculars PL, PM, PN are drawn to QT, RT, QR respectively. Show that $PN^2 = (PL)(PM)$.

12. L is the midpoint of the side BC of triangle ABC. The circle through L which touches AB at B and the circle through L which touches AC at C meet again at D. Prove that $(LA)(LD) = LB^2$.

13. Given a circle S and two points external to it, provide a construction for a circle passing through the two given points and touching S.

Theorem 5 (Ptolemy's Theorem)

If $ABCD$ is a cyclic quadrilateral, then

$$(AB)(CD) + (BC)(DA) = (AC)(BD).$$

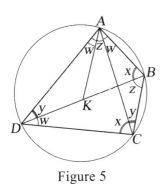

Figure 5

Proof

Locate the point K on BD such that $\angle DAK = \angle CAB$. Now

$$\angle KDA = \angle BDA - \angle BCA$$

(angles in the same segment). Hence triangles ADK and ACB are similar. Therefore

$$AD : DK = AC : CB$$

or put another way

$$(BC)(DA) = (AC)(DK).$$

Now $\angle KAB = \angle KAC + \angle CAB = \angle KAC + \angle DAK = \angle DAC$, and $\angle ACD = \angle ABD$ (angles in the same segment) $= \angle ABK$. Hence triangles AKB and ADC are similar. Therefore $AB : KB = AC : DC$ or $(AB)(CD) = (AC)(KB)$. Summing the two equations obtained we have

$$(AB)(CD)+(BC)(DA) = (AC)(KB)+(AC)(DK) = (AC)(BD).$$

∎

Exercises

14. Prove that, if $w + x + y + z = 180^0$, then

$$\sin y \sin z + \sin w \sin x = \sin(w + z) \sin(x + z).$$

By identifying w, x, y, z with the angles in Figure 5, provide a second proof of Ptolemy's theorem.

15. P is a point on the minor arc BC of the circumcircle of an equilateral triangle ABC. Prove that $PA = PB + PC$.

16. P is a point of the minor arc AB of the circumcircle of the square $ABCD$. Prove that $PC(PA+PC) = PD(PB+PD)$.

17. P is a point inside a parallelogram $ABCD$ such that

$$\angle\, APB + \angle CPD = 180^o.$$

Prove that $(AP)(CP) + (BP)(DP) = (AB)(BC)$.

18. P is a point on the minor arc AB of the circumcircle of a regular pentagon $ABCDE$. Prove that

$$PA + PB + PD = PC + PE.$$

3.4   Unit 2: Hints and Solutions

1. They are at the opposite ends of the diameter perpendicular to the given direction.

2. Consider all lines through the external point.

3. In triangles TAP and TPB we have $\angle PTA = \angle BTP$ is common and $TP/TB = TA/TP$, so these triangles are similar. In particular $\angle APT = \angle PBT = \angle PBA$. Hence, by the converse of the alternate segment theorem, the circle PAB touches TP at P.

4. Let BB_0 and C_0C meet at P. Draw the tangents AQ and AR to the circles at A and let $\angle QAR = x$ be the angle of intersection of the two circles. Then, by the alternate segment theorem, $\angle ABQ = \angle AB_0Q = \angle ACR = \angle AC_0R = x$. Also $\angle BB_0Q = \angle BAQ = z$ (say) and $\angle C_0CR = \angle C_0AR = y$ (say). Then $\angle BPC = 360^\circ - (180^\circ - x - z) - (180^\circ - x - y) - (x + y + z) = x = $ constant .

5. QM is parallel to PB since $\angle AQM = \angle APB = 90^\circ$. Similarly RM is parallel to PA. Now $QPRM$ is a rectangle so is a cyclic quadrilateral. Hence $\angle MQR = \angle MPR = 90^\circ - \angle MBR = \angle PAM = \angle QAM$. It follows by the converse of the alternate segment theorem that QR touches circle AQM at Q. Similarly QR touches circle BRM at R.

6. Let the common chord be XY. Since the circles cut at right angles, the tangent at X to the first circle passes through B. By the tangent chord theorem $(BE)(BD) = (BX)^2$. Now $\angle AXB = \angle XFA = 90^\circ$, so $\angle FXB = \angle XAB$. It follows that triangles FXB and XAB are similar and hence $(BX)^2 = (BF)(BA)$. We now have $(BF)(BA) = (BE)(BD)$,

so by the converse of the intersecting chord theorem A, D, E, F are concyclic.

7. Let the common tangent at A meet PR at L and PQ at M. Now $LA = LR$, both being tangents from L, so $\angle LRA = \angle LAR = \angle QAM$. But by the alternate segment theorem $\angle LRA = \angle RTA$ and $\angle QAM = \angle QPA$. Hence $\angle QPA = \angle RTA$ and since PAT is a straight line this means that PQ and RT are parallel.

8. Suppose that an inscribed circle exists and touches AB, BC, CD, DA at W, X, Y, Z respectively, then we have $a = AZ = AW, b = BW = BX, c = CX = CY, d = DY = DZ$ (tangents from an external point equal in length). Then $AB + CD = BC + DA = a + b + c + d$. Conversely a rhombus has an incircle and if $ABCD$ is not a rhombus we may choose a pair of opposite sides which are not parallel, say AD and BC, to meet at P. Let S be the incircle of triangle ABP and let the tangent from C to S meet AP at E. Then S is an inscribed circle to $ABCE$ and hence, by the first part, $AB + CE = BC + EA$. Hence $DE = EA - DA = CE - CD$. Triangle CDE therefore degenerates and D coincides with E.

9. $\angle CTB = \angle TAB$ by the alternate segment theorem. But $\angle DTB = \angle DCA = 90^{o}$. Hence $\angle CDT = \angle CTD$, so that $CT = CD$.

10. Arc TP =arc TQ, since both arcs subtend equal angles at A. It follows that chord $TP =$ chord TQ and thus PQ is parallel to the tangent at T.

11. $LQNP$ is cyclic since $\angle QLP = \angle QNP = 90^{o}$. Similarly $NRMP$ is cyclic. Hence $\angle PLN = \angle PQN$ (angles in the

same segment) $= \angle PRM$ (alternate segment theorem) $=$ $\angle PNM$ (angles in the same segment). Similarly $\angle PNL =$ $\angle PMN$. It follows that triangles PLN and PNM are similar, so that $PL/PN = PN/PM$; that is, $(PL)(PM) = (PN)^2$.

12. Note that $\angle ABL = \angle BDL$ (alternate segment theorem); similarly $\angle ACL = \angle CDL$. It follows that

$$\angle BDL + \angle CDL + \angle BAC = 180^o$$

and hence $ABDC$ is cyclic. Now let DL meet circle $ABDC$ again at E. If E is the same point as A the result follows immediately by the intersecting chord theorem. Otherwise, $\angle EAB = \angle EDB = \angle ABC$ and AB is thus parallel to BC. In this case the figure $AEBC$ is a trapezium inscribed in a circle and L, the midpoint of BC, is equidistant from A and E. Hence $LA = LE$ and the result again follows from the intersecting chord theorem $(LB)(LC) = (LE)(LD)$.

13. If A, B are the two points, draw any circle through A and B to intersect S at C and D. Let AB and CD meet at P. Draw PQ to touch S at Q. Then ABQ is the required circle. For, by construction, $(PA)(PB) = (PC)(PD) = (PQ)^2$. So by the converse of the tangent chord theorem (Exercise 3) the circle ABQ touches PQ at Q.

14. $\sin(w + z)\sin(x + z) - \sin w \sin x$
$= \sin(x + y)\sin(x + z) - \sin(x + y + z)\sin x$
$= \frac{1}{2}(\cos(y - z) - \cos(2x + y + z) - \cos(y + z) + \cos(2x + y + z))$
$= \sin y \sin z$.

Ptolemy's theorem follows since a chord of a circle of radius R subtending an angle x at the circumference is of length $2R \sin x$. See Figure 5.

15. Ptolemy's theorem for the cyclic quadrilateral $ABPC$ produces the result immediately.

16. Ptolemy's theorem for the quadrilaterals $PCDA$ and $PBCD$ yields

$$
\begin{aligned}
(PA)(CD) + (PC)(AD) &= (PD)(AC) \text{ and} \\
(PB)(CD) + (PD)(BC) &= (PC)(BD).
\end{aligned}
$$

Dividing these equations and noting $AC = BD = \sqrt{2} \times$ side length of the square, one derives the required result by cross multiplication.

17. Choose the point Q on the other side of DC to P so that triangles ABP and DCQ are congruent. Since AB and DC are parallel it is evident that BP and CQ are equal and parallel. It follows that the figure $PBCQ$ is a parallelogram and in particular $PQ = BC$. Now apply Ptolemy's theorem to the quadrilateral $DPCQ$, this being a cyclic quadrilateral since $\angle DQC + \angle DPC = \angle APB + \angle DPC = 180^o$. One obtains $(DP)(CQ) + (PC)(QD) = (PQ)(DC) = (BC)(AB)$, from which the result follows.

18. Apply Ptolemy's theorem three times to $PBDA, APBC$ and $EAPB$, to get $(PB)(DA) + (PA)(BD) = (PD)(AB)$ and $(AP)(BC) + (PB)(CA) = (AB)(PC)$. Now DA, BD, CA and BE are all diagonals of the pentagon, so are of the form ka, where a is the side length of the pentagon and k is a constant. The above three equations can now be written as $PD = k(PB + PA), PC = kPB + AP$ and $PE = PB + kAP$ from which $PC + PE = (k+1)(PB + PA) = PA + PB + PD$.

3.5 Unit 3: The centres of similitude of two circles

Definition

Let S_1 and S_2 be two circles with centres C_1 and C_2 and radii r_1 and r_2 respectively. Define V and W to be the points on C_1C_2 dividing it externally and internally in the ratio of the radii. That is, $VC_1/VC_2 = C_1W/WC_2 = r_1/r_2$. Note that the ordering of the letters implies that V is to one side of C_1 and C_2 and that W lies between them. V and W are called the **external** and **internal** **centres of similitude** of S_1 and S_2.

If S_1 and S_2 have equal radii then W is the midpoint of C_1C_2 and V does not exist (or can be thought of as being at infinity in the direction of C_1C_2). In this case S_1 is mapped on to S_2 by a translation or by a rotation of 180° about W. When the radii are unequal with $r_2 > r_1$, then S_1 is mapped on to S_2 by an enlargement, centre V and scale factor r_2/r_1 or by a rotation of 180° about W followed by an enlargement, centre W and scale factor r_2/r_1.

These definitions and their interpretation in terms of transformations are the same whether the circles lie external to each other, as in Figure 1, or intersect one another or lie one inside the other.

Theorem 1

(a) Let P_1 and P_2 be two points on S_1 and S_2 respectively then P_1P_2 passes through V if and only if C_1P_1 and C_2P_2 are parallel and P_1 and P_2 lie on the same side of C_1C_2.

(b) Let P_1 and Q_2 be two points on S_1 and S_2 respectively then P_1Q_2 passes through W if and only if C_1P_1 and C_2Q_2 are parallel and P_1 and Q_2 lie on opposite sides of C_1C_2.

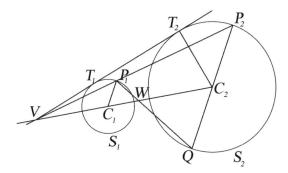

Figure 1

The proof of this theorem is a straightforward application of ideas involving similar triangles and is left to the reader.

Exercises

1. Prove that the common tangents to two circles (of unequal radii) pass through one or other of the centres of similitude.

2. Two circles S_1 and S_2 intersect at A and B and their common tangents intersect at T. AP and AQ are the tangents at A to the two circles. Prove that AT bisects $\angle PAQ$.

3. The centres of two circles of unequal radii r_1, r_2 are a distance r_{12} apart. Calculate the distance between the two centres of similitude.

4. Two fixed circles S_1 and S_2 touch each other at T. A variable line through T cuts the circles at P_1 and P_2 respectively. Prove that $TP_1/TP_2 = r_1/r_2$, where r_1 and r_2 are the radii of S_1 and S_2 respectively.

5. Two circles AP_1Q_1 and AP_2Q_2 cut at A. The lines P_1P_2, Q_1Q_2 are their common tangents. Prove that the circles AP_1P_2 and AQ_1Q_2 touch each other.

It is possible for pairs of triangles (or other polygons) to have either one or two centres of similitude, and when this occurs the figures concerned are not only similar but corresponding sides are parallel. Some authors use the phrase **directly similar** or alternatively the word **homothetic** to describe this situation.

A triangle and its median triangle

As an example of this consider a triangle ABC and its medians AL, BM, CN. Triangle LMN is called the median triangle.

Since L, M, N are the midpoints of the sides BC, CA, AB respectively the theory of similar triangles implies that NM is parallel to BC and is half its length. Similarly LN is parallel to CA and is half its length and ML is parallel to AB and is half its length. Triangle ABC is an enlargement of triangle LMN with scale factor 2, but LMN is also inverted with respect to triangle ABC. Furthermore, it is an elementary property of the triangle that the medians AL, BM, CN are concurrent at the centroid G of triangle ABC and that $AG/GL = BG/GM = CG/GN = 2/1$. G is therefore the internal centre of similitude of the two triangles.

Suppose now that we draw the circle through ABC and the circle through LMN. The former is called the **circumcircle** of ABC and the latter is called its **nine-point circle**. (The name originates from the fact that it passes through six other key points connected with triangle ABC besides L, M, N.) It is clear that if the radius of the circumcircle is R, then the radius of the nine-point circle is $\frac{1}{2}R$. Now let the centre O of the circumcircle be the origin of vectors and $\mathbf{x}, \mathbf{y}, \mathbf{z}$ be the vector positions of A, B, C

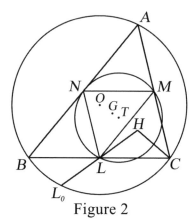

Figure 2

respectively, then it is well known that G has position vector

$$\frac{1}{3}(\mathbf{x} + \mathbf{y} + \mathbf{z}).$$

It follows that the centre T of the nine-point circle is

$$\frac{1}{2}(\mathbf{x} + \mathbf{y} + \mathbf{z}).$$

If we now forget about the triangles and just concentrate on the two circles, then they must have an external centre of similitude (say H) as well as an internal one. This must lie on the line OGT and must be situated so that $OH = 2TH$, from which it follows that H has position vector $\mathbf{x} + \mathbf{y} + \mathbf{z}$. Several interesting geometrical facts about this figure now follow immediately. For example if HL meets the circumcircle at L_0, then $HL = LL_0$, with similar results for the lines HM and HN. Also the midpoints of AH, BH and CH must lie on the nine-point circle. We meet this configuration again in Unit 5, when other geometrical properties of the point H are demonstrated.

3.6 Unit 3: Hints and Solutions

1. Suppose that the tangent from V to S_1 touches it at T_1. Drop the perpendicular from C_2 on to VT_1. Then triangles VT_1C_1 and VT_2C_2 are similar, having equal angles. It follows that $r_2/r_1 = VC_2/VC_1 = VT_2/VT_1 = VT_2/r_1$. Hence $VT_2 = r_2$ and is therefore a radius of S_2 and touches it at T_2.

2. As T is a centre of similitude, we have $TD/TA = r_2/r_1$ and $TA/TC = r_2/r_1$. Now write $TC = x, CA = y$ and $AD = z$, then $(x+y+z)/(x+y) = r_2/r_1$ and $(x+y)/x = r_2/r_1$. It follows that $z/(x+y) = (r_2-r_1)/r_1$ and $y/(x+y) = (r_2-r_1)/r_2$. Hence $y/z = r_1/r_2 = CA/AD$. This means AC and AD subtend equal angles in S_1 and S_2. The result now follows from the alternate segment theorem.

3. $VW = \dfrac{2r_1r_2r_{12}}{(r_2^2 - r_1^2)}.$

4. This follows immediately, since T is either an external or internal centre of similitude.

5. Let TA meet S_1 at A_1 and S_2 at A_2 and write $r_2/r_1 = k$, where T is the external centre of similitude. Explain why the following four equations hold: (i) $TA = kTA_1$; (ii) $TA_2 = kTA$; (iii) $(TA_1)(TA) = TP_1^2$ (iv) $(TA)(TA_2) = TP_2^2$. Deduce from these that $(TP_1)(TP_2) = TA^2$ and use the converse of Theorem 4 (the intersecting chord and tangent theorem) to show that TA is tangent to the circle AP_1P_2 at A. Similarly TA is tangent to circle TQ_1Q_2 at A. This means that circles S_1 and S_2 touch at A.

Chapter 4

Triangles

4.1 Unit 4: Notation and Revision Exercises

Introduction

In this chapter the more advanced properties of the triangle and its circles are studied, using purely geometrical and trigonometrical methods. In later chapters vector and co-ordinate methods are also employed. This involves some repetition, but provides additional insight and allows the student a variety of methods to choose from when solving problems.

Notation

In triangle ABC the lengths of sides BC, CA and AB are denoted by a, b and c respectively. The feet of the perpendiculars dropped from A, B and C to the sides BC, CA and AB are denoted D, E and F respectively, and we write $AD = d, BE = e$ and $CF = f$.

The **orthocentre** is the point where these perpendiculars meet and is denoted by H. L, M and N denote the midpoints of the sides BC, CA and AB respectively. AL, BM and CN meet at the **centroid** G, and we write $AL = l, BM = m$ and $CN = n$. The circle passing through the vertices A, B and C is called the **circumcircle**. Its centre O is called the **circumcentre** of triangle ABC. R denotes its radius. The circle touching the sides BC, CA and AB internally is called the **incircle**. Its centre I is called the **incentre** of triangle ABC. Its radius is denoted by r. The lines AI, BI and CI meet the sides BC, CA and AB at points denoted U, V and W respectively and we write $AU = u, BV = v$ and $CW = w$. Let X, Y and Z denote the points where the incircle touches the sides BC, CA and AB respectively.

The circle through L, M and N also passes through D, E and F and is known as the **nine-point circle**. Its centre, T is called the **nine-point centre**.

Let I_1, I_2 and I_3 denote the centres of the **escribed circles** opposite A, B and C respectively. The points where the escribed circles touch the sides BC, CA and AB are respectively denoted X_j, Y_j and Z_j ($j = 1,$ 2 and 3). The radii of the escribed circles are denoted by r_1, r_2 and r_3.

The **semi-perimeter** is written $s = \frac{1}{2}(a + b + c)$. The area of triangle ABC is denoted by $[ABC]$ and square brackets surrounding any three points denotes the area of the triangle formed by the lines through those points.

Assumed knowledge

In general, results in Chapters 1-3 are assumed known, but attention is drawn particularly to the sine and cosine rules of trigonometry and elementary results concerning the centroid G, and circumcentre O, proved in Chapter 2. We start proceedings by quoting these results and providing a set of exercises designed to reinforce the ideas involved and to extend those ideas using the theory from Chapter 3 on circles.

$$\text{THE SINE RULE} \quad \frac{a}{\sin A} = \frac{b}{\sin B} = \frac{c}{\sin C} = 2R.$$

$$\text{THE COSINE RULE} \quad a^2 = b^2 + c^2 - 2bc \cos A$$
$$\text{or} \quad \cos A = (b^2 + c^2 - a^2)/2bc.$$

There are four similar results to these formed by cyclic change of the letters a, b and c and A, B and C.

Theorem 1 (Centroid property)

The lines AL, BM and CN are concurrent at the centroid G, and $AG = (2/3)AL$ etc.

Theorem 2 (Circumcentre property)

The perpendiculars to BC through L, to CA through M and AB through N are concurrent at O, and O is the centre of the circumcircle passing through A, B and C.

Exercises

1. Prove that the circumcircle of triangle ANM passes through O and has the radius $\frac{1}{2}R$.

2. Prove that $bc = 2Rd, ca = 2Re, ab = 2Rf$.

3. Two triangles A_1BC and A_2BC have a common base BC. If A_1A_2 meets BC at A_0 then

$$[A_1BC] : [A_2BC] = A_1A_0 : A_2A_0.$$

4. Prove that G is the centroid of triangle LMN and that

$$[LMG] = [MNG] = [NLG] = \frac{1}{12}[ABC].$$

5. ABC is a triangle and P lies on BC (possibly on its extension).
   Prove that
$$BP/PC = \frac{AB \times \sin(\angle BAP)}{AC \times \sin(\angle PAC)}.$$

6. The diagonals AC, BD of a cyclic quadrilateral meet at P.
   Prove that
$$\frac{(AB)(BC)}{(AD)(DC)} = BP/PD.$$

7. Two circles touch internally at O. A straight line $ABCD$ cuts the outer circle at A, D and the inner circle at B, C. Prove that

$$AB : CD = (OA)(OB) : (OC)(OD).$$

8. Show how to calculate the sides and angles of a triangle in which the side a and $\angle A$ are given and also the product of the other two sides $bc = m^2$ is given.

9. In a certain triangle $a > b > c, a = 2c$ and $A = 2B$. Prove that $a : b : c = 17156 : 13395 : 8578$ approximately, and that

$$4\cos^2 B = 1 + \cos B.$$

10. ABC is a triangle and L is the midpoint of BC. Prove Apollonius's Theorem that

$$(AL)^2 = \frac{1}{4}(2b^2 + 2c^2 - a^2).$$

11. A_0, B_0, C_0 are the angles subtended at the centroid G of the triangle ABC by the sides. Prove that

$$\cot A - \cot A_0 = \cot B - \cot B_0 = \cot C - \cot C_0$$
$$= \frac{2}{3}(\cot A + \cot B + \cot C).$$

12. A and B are two fixed points. P moves so that PA/PB is a constant (not equal to unity). Prove that the locus of P is a circle. (**The circle of Apollonius**)

13. Prove there exists a point Ω inside triangle ABC such that $\angle BA\Omega = \angle CB\Omega = \angle AC\Omega = \omega$ say. Prove also that

$$\cot \omega = \cot A + \cot B + \cot C$$

(Ω is one of two **Brocard** points of triangle ABC, the other being Ω', where $\angle AB\Omega' = \angle BC\Omega' = \angle CA\Omega' = \omega$. If ABC is equilateral the two points coincide.)

14. In triangle ABC the midpoint of BC is denoted by L. Let P and R be points on AB and AC respectively and let Q be the intersection of AL and PR. Prove that if Q is the midpoint of PR, then PR is parallel to BC.

4.2   Unit 4: Hints and solutions

1. $\angle ANO = \angle AMO = 90^o$, so AO is the diameter of circle ANM and is of length R.

2. Remember that $[ABC] = \frac{1}{2}ad = \frac{abc}{4R}$.

3. Drop perpendiculars from A_1 and A_2 to meet BC in D_1 and D_2 and then use similar triangles to compare the heights of the triangles A_1BC and A_2BC.

4. Let AL meet NM in F, then since $BL = LC$, it follows that $NF = FM$. Hence LGF is a median of triangle LMN. Similarly its other two medians pass through G, which is therefore the centroid of triangle LMN. Now $GF = \frac{1}{6}AL$ and $MN = \frac{1}{2}BC$, so $[GMN] = \frac{1}{12}[ABC]$.

5. $[ABC] = \frac{1}{2}(AB)(AP)\sin(\angle BAP)$
   $= \frac{1}{2}(BP) \times$ height of triangle ABC. Divide this by a similar expression for $[ACP]$ and the result follows.

6. Use the solution to Question 5 on triangle ADB with P on DB to give

$$BP/PD = \frac{(AB)\sin(\angle BAC)}{(AD)\sin(\angle DAC)}.$$

Now $\angle BAC = \angle BDC$ and $\angle DAC = \angle DBC$. Finally the sine rule on triangle BCD converts the ratio of sines to the required extra factors $(BC)/(DC)$.

7. Draw the common tangent OT at O. Then $\angle DOT = \angle BAO$ (alternate segment theorem). Similarly $\angle COT = \angle CBO$. Subtraction gives $\angle AOB = \angle COD$. Now use pairs of expressions for each of the areas of triangles AOB and COD,

8. Write $b = mk$ and $c = m/k$ and use the cosine rule with $\angle A$ to get a quadratic equation in k^2. You should find a condition on a, A and m for a triangle to exist.

9. $\sin A = \sin 2B = 2 \sin B \cos B$. It follows that $a = 2b \cos B$. The cosine rule for B yields the trigonometric equation for $\cos B$, after factorization. The numerical part can be checked.

10. Complete the parallelogram $ACDB$, so that $(AD)^2 = 4(AL)^2$
    $= b^2 + c^2 - 2bc \cos(B+C) = b^2 + c^2 + 2bc \cos A = 2b^2 + 2c^2 - a^2$
    where we have used the cosine rule twice.

11. Use the cosine rule for $\cos A$ and the formula $[ABC] = \frac{1}{2}bc \sin A$ to show
    $$\cot A = (b^2 + c^2 - a^2)/4[ABC]$$

    Use Apollonius's Theorem for the sides GB, GC of triangle GBC, the cosine rule for $\cos A_0$ and the formula $[GBC] = \frac{1}{2}(GB)(GC) \sin A_0$ to show
    $$\cot A_0 = \frac{b^2 + c^2 - 5a^2}{12[ABC]}.$$

    The result follows immediately, and the symmetry of the expression proves the equalities using B, C instead of A.

12. Define points U and U_0 on AB, such that U lies internally and U_0 lies on the extension of AB and $UA/UB = U_0A/U_0B = PA/PB$. Then by the sine rule, for any fixed position of P, PU is the internal bisector of angle APB. It follows that $\angle UPU_0 = 90^o$. Since U and U_0 are fixed points this means that P lies on the circle with UU_0 as diameter.

13. Draw the circle through A and C touching AB at A, and the circle through B and A touching BC at B. Let them

meet at Ω. Then the alternate segment theorem shows the stated angles are equal and that the circle through C, B and Ω touches CA at C. Three applications of the sine rule followed by multiplication to eliminate $A\Omega$, $B\Omega$, $C\Omega$ produces the equation

$$\sin^3 \omega = \sin(A - \omega)\sin(B - \omega)\sin(C - \omega),$$

from which the given relationship may be deduced by trigonometric manipulation.

14. The proof is by contradiction. Supoose that PR is not parallel to BC and that these lines meet at K. Then consider the fraction

$$\frac{(BL)(CK)}{(LC)(BK)}$$

and show by means of areas it is equal to the fraction

$$\frac{(PQ)(RK)}{(QR)(PK)}.$$

These fractions are called cross ratios when they involve four points on a line in this manner. The data now implies $CK/BK = RK/PK$. This implies that triangles PBK and RCK are similar, which from the figure is patently false, AB and AC not being parallel. (This is a case when the converse of a trivial result is far from easy to prove, something in Geometry one meets quite frequently.)

4.3 Unit 5: Orthocentre and Nine-Point Circle

Theorem 1 (Orthocentre property)

The altitudes AD, BE, CF are concurrent.

The point of concurrency H is called the **orthocentre** of triangle ABC.

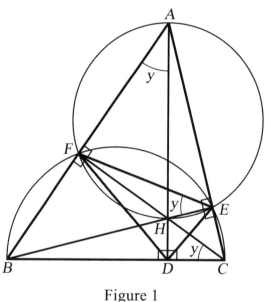

Figure 1

If any of angles A, B, C is equal to 90° the theorem is trivial, the orthocentre being at the vertex concerned. In Figure 1 we show the diagram when triangle ABC is acute. The proof given here is for this case. When one of the angles is obtuse a similar proof is needed with appropriate alterations and the reader is encouraged to construct a proof as an exercise. The point H in the case of an obtuse angled triangle lies outside the triangle.

1st Proof

Let BE and CF meet at H. Let AH extended meet BC at D. The theorem is proved by showing that $\angle ADC = 90^o$. Since $\angle CFA =$

$\angle BFC = 90^o$ and $\angle BEC = \angle AEB = 90^o$ both $AEHF$ and $BFEC$ are cyclic quadrilaterals. The circles involved are drawn in Figure 1. It follows that $\angle FAH = \angle FEH = \angle FCB$(angles in the same segment). In particular $\angle FAD = \angle FCD$ and this implies by the converse of the angles in the same segment theorem that $AFDC$ is cyclic. Hence $\angle ADC = \angle AFC = 90^o$. The common angle y used in the proof and marked on Figure 1 is equal to $90^o - B$, and similarly we define $x = 90^o - A$ and $z = 90^o - C$. ■

The triangle DEF is called the **pedal triangle**.

The second proof is quite crafty, though perhaps not as illuminating as the first proof, and uses the known circumcentre property.

2nd Proof
Define B_0, C_0 so that $ACBC_0$ and $CBAB_0$ are parallelograms. Let C_0B and B_0C meet at A_0. Then $BACA_0$ is also a parallelogram and A, B, C are the midpoints of B_0C_0, C_0A_0, A_0B_0 respectively. The perpendicular B_0C_0 through A is also perpendicular to BC, since B_0C_0 and BC are parallel. The three such perpendiculars meet at the circumcentre of triangle $A_0B_0C_0$ and as these are the altitudes of triangle ABC so they too are concurrent. ■

Theorem 2

In an acute angled triangle ABC the altitudes bisect the angles of the pedal triangle and the angles of the pedal triangle are $\angle FDE = 180^o - 2A, \angle DEF = 180^o - 2B, \angle EFD = 180^o - 2C$.

Proof
Referring back to Figure 1, we can see that $HECD$ is cyclic, since angle ADC has been proved equal to 90°, it follows that $\angle HED = \angle HCD = y$. Hence BE bisects $\angle FED$, which is equal

to $2y = 180° - 2B$. Similar arguments hold for the angles at vertices F and D. ■

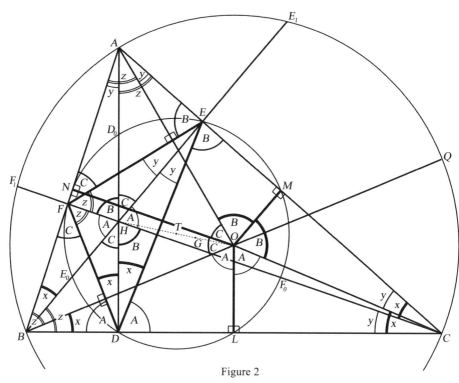

Figure 2

Figure 2 shows how the altitudes and other important lines, such as AO, BO, CO, OL, OM, ON divide up the angles at A, B, C, O and H. Derivations of the results shown are straightforward and some appear as problems in the following set of Exercises. In these exercises you should suppose triangle ABC is acute and, for particularity, that $A > B > C$. Corresponding results exist in other cases. Results of some of the questions are used in the text that follows.

Exercises

1. (a) Prove that the angles of the pedal triangle are
    $180^{o} - 2A, 180^{o} - 2B, 180^{o} - 2C$.

    (b) Prove $\angle CDE = \angle FDB = A$. Prove also that $\angle LBO = 90^{o} - A$.

    (c) Prove that BO is perpendicular to FD.

2. Prove that triangle AEF is similar to triangle ABC and deduce that $EF = a \cos A = R \sin 2A$. Show further that the radius of the circumcircle of the pedal triangle is $\frac{1}{2}R$.

3. Prove that $AH = a \cot A = 2R \cos A$.

4. Prove that $HD = 2R \cos B \cos C$.

5. Prove that A, B, C are the orthocentres of triangles HBC, HCA, HAB respectively.

6. Prove that the circumcentre of triangle ABC is the orthocentre of triangle LMN.

7. Let CF meet the circumcircle of triangle ABC at F_1 Prove that $HF = FF_1$ and that $AF_1 = AH$.

8. Let the extension of BO meet the circumcircle again at Q. Prove that $AQCH$ is a parallelogram.

The Nine-Point Circle and Euler Line

A brief introductory account of the Nine-Point Circle has been given at the end of Unit 3, but the following derivation is quite independent of that account. Here we define the **Nine-Point Circle** to be the circumcircle of the pedal triangle DEF. To find **nine** points we need to identify six other key points through which the circle passes, and we also locate its centre as the midpoint of the line segment OH.

From Exercise 2 we know that the radius of the circle is $\frac{1}{2}R$. From Exercise 7 we know that $HD = \frac{1}{2}HD_1, HE = \frac{1}{2}HE_1, HF = \frac{1}{2}HF_1$. It follows from these facts that H is the external centre of similitude of the circles DEF and ABC. This implies that the centre T of the circle DEF lies on HO and satisfies $HT = \frac{1}{2}HO$. See Figure 2 which shows the **Euler line** HO, with T the midpoint of HO. Now let D_0, E_0, F_0 be the midpoints of AH, BH, CH respectively. Then $HD_0 = \frac{1}{2}HA, HE_0 = \frac{1}{2}HB, HF_0 = \frac{1}{2}HC$. It follows that D_0, E_0, F_0 lie on the Nine-Point Circle and constitute three more of the nine key points in the circle.

Further from Exercise 8 we know that $AQCH$ is a parallelogram, and as M is the midpoint of the diagonal AC, it is also the midpoint of diagonal HQ. This means that $HM = \frac{1}{2}HQ$. But Q lies on the circumcircle, so M lies on circle DEF. Similarly L, N lie on this circle too. Thus, L, M, N are the three remaining key points of the Nine-Point Circle.

Exercises

9. Prove that $AD_0 = OL$ and hence that $AOLD_0$ is a parallelogram. Prove further that LD_0 passes through T and is therefore a diameter of the Nine-Point Circle.

10. Show that the centroid G is the internal centre of similitude of the Nine-Point Circle and the circumcircle of triangle ABC. Deduce that G lies on the Euler line OTH and that $GT = \frac{1}{2}OG$.

11. Let the extension of DG meet the circumcircle again at D_2. Prove that $GD = \frac{1}{2}D_2G$.

12. Prove that the figure NMF_0E_0 is a rectangle.

13. Let P_0 be the point on the Nine-Point Circle one third of the way along the arc from L to D; and let Q_0 and R_0 be defined similarly on the arcs ME and NF. Prove that triangle $P_0Q_0R_0$ is equilateral.

14. Let AO meet BC at K. Prove that the $\angle BOK = 180^\circ - 2C$, and hence that $\angle KOL = |(B - C)|$. Show further that

$$OK = \frac{R\cos A}{\cos(B - C)}$$

and deduce that

$$\frac{OK}{AK} = \frac{1}{2}(1 - \cot B \cot C).$$

15. Prove that $\angle FD_0N = |A - B|$.

16. Prove that the perimeter of the pedal triangle is $2[ABC]/R$.

17. Prove that LD_0 is perpendicular to EF.

18. If O_A, O_B, O_C are the reflections of O in the sides BC, CA, AB respectively, prove that AO_A, BO_B, CO_C are concurrent.

4.4   Unit 5: Hints and Solutions

1. For part (a) see the text to Theorem 2. Part (b) follows from the fact that $\angle ADE = x$. For part (c) note that LO bisects the angle at O into two parts both equal to A. So $\angle BOL = A$. It follows that the $\angle OBL = x$. Now observe that $\angle FDB = A$ and the result follows.

2. See Figure 2 for the first part. Then using the similarity we have $EF/a = AE/c = c \cos A/c$ and hence $EF = a \cos A = 2R \sin A \cos A = R \sin 2A$. Now if R_0 is the radius of triangle DEF, then

$$EF = 2R_0 \sin FDE = 2R_0 \sin(180^o - 2A) = 2R_0 \sin 2A.$$

It follows from the previous result that $R_0 = \frac{1}{2}R$.

3. $AH = AF \operatorname{cosec} B = b \cos A \operatorname{cosec} B = 2R \cos A = a \cot A$.

4. $HD = BH \cos C$, which by Exercise 3 is $2R \cos B \cos C$.

5. Draw a diagram with the appropriate perpendiculars.

6. The result follows from exactly the same argument as in the 2nd proof of Theorem 1.

7. $\angle AF_1C = \angle ABC$, so triangle AF_1H is isosceles and since $\angle AFC = 90^o$ triangles AF_1F and AHF are congruent. The results now follow immediately.

8. $\angle QCF_1 = \angle QBF_1$ (angles in the same segment) $= \angle QBF + \angle FBF_1 = z + x = B$. Hence AH is parallel to QC since both make an angle B with CH. Now BOQ is a diameter of the circumcircle, so $QC = 2R = \sin QBC = 2R \sin x = 2R \cos A = AH$ (see Exercise 3). Hence $AQCH$ is a parallelogram.

9. $AD_0 = D_0H = OL = R\cos A$ and all three lines are parallel. It follows that both $AOLD_0$ and D_0OLH are parallelograms. Now T is the midpoint of the diagonal OH and is therefore the midpoint of LD_0.

10. This follows from the fact that $GL = \frac{1}{2}AG, GM = \frac{1}{2}BG, GN = \frac{1}{2}CG$, the radii of two circles being in the ratio 1:2. For the second part note that both centres of similtude lie on the line of centres TO and hence $GT = \frac{1}{2}OG$ as well.

11. D which lies on the Nine-Point Circle and D_2 which lies on the the circumcircle are corresponding points through the centre of similitude.

12. E_0M and F_0N are of equal length both being diameters of the Nine-Point Circle and both have the centre T as their midpoints.

13. Define P_1 on the circumcircle such that $HP_0 = P_0P_1$ and let Q_1, R_1 be defined similarly. Now HM meets the circumcircle in Q, so Q_1 is one third of the way along the arc from Q to E_1 (the point where HE meets the circumcircle). Now find the angular orientation of the points P_1, Q_1, R_1 around the circumcircle, using the angle properties shown in Figure 2. You will find $\angle Q_1OR_1 = 120^o$.

14. For the first part use $\angle KOL = \angle DAO = z - y$. For the second part use trigonometrical ratios in triangles LOK and DAK. Remember also that $\cos A = -\cos(B + C)$.

15. $\angle FD_0N = \frac{1}{2}\angle FTN = \frac{1}{2}\angle F_1OR = \angle F_1CR = y - x$. (Here R is the point where CO meets the circumcircle again.)

16. From Exercise 2 we have $EF = R\sin 2A$. Now use

$$\sin 2A + \sin 2B + \sin 2C \quad 4\sin A \sin B \sin C = abc/(2R^3)$$

and $[ABC] = abc/4R$.

17. LD_0 is parallel to OA.

18. AOO_AH is a parallelogram and so AO_A passes through T.

4.5 Unit 6: The Incircle and Excircles

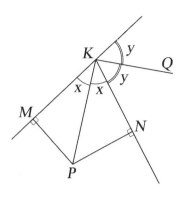

Figure 1 shows a pair of lines meeting at a point K and the internal and external bisectors KP and KQ respectively of the angle formed at K. M and N are the feet of the perpendiculars on to the lines from P. In triangles KMP and KNP we have OP common, $\angle MKP = \angle NKP$, marked as x in the figure, and

$$\angle PMK = \angle PNK = 90^{o}.$$

Figure 1

It follows that the triangles are congruent and hence $PM = PN$. Therefore the internal bisector is equidistant from the two lines.

Likewise Q is equidistant from the two lines or their extensions. The angle marked y in the figure is half the external angle at K and since $2x + 2y = 180^{o}$ we have $\angle PKQ = x + y = 90^{o}$. The internal and external bisectors of an angle are at right angles.

Theorem 1

The internal bisectors of the angles of triangle ABC are concurrent at a point I, and I is the centre of the incircle, which touches AB, BC, CA internally.

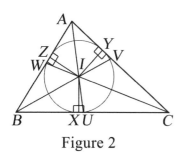

Figure 2

Proof

Let the bisectors BV and CW meet at I. Since I lies on the bisector BV the perpendiculars IZ and IX are equal. Since I lies on the bisector CW the perpendiculars IX and IY are equal. Hence $IY = IZ$. Now in triangles AIZ and AIY we have $IY = IZ$ (proved), AI is common and $\angle AZI = \angle AYI = 90^o$. Hence the triangles are congruent, and it follows that AI is the internal bisector of $\angle BAC$.   ∎

The circle centre I and radius $r = IX = IY = IZ$ touches the sides BC, CA, AB at X, Y, Z respectively. This circle is called the **inscribed circle** or **incircle**. I is called the **incentre**.

Theorem 2

In triangle ABC the internal bisector of $\angle BAC$ and the external bisectors of $\angle CBA$ and $\angle ACB$ are concurrent at a point I_1, and I_1 is the centre of the escribed circle opposite A, which touches BC internally and the extensions of AB, AC.

As the proof is virtually identical to that of Theorem 1 it is omitted. The radius of the **escribed circle** or **excircle** opposite A is denoted by $r_1 = I_1X_1 = I_1Y_1 = I_1Z_1$. The radii of the escribed circles opposite B, C are denoted by r_2, r_3 respectively.

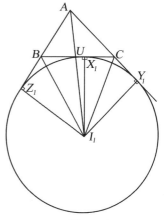

Figure 3

We now provide a list of formulae, followed by a set of exercises, the results of which connect the radii of the inscribed and escribed circles and the sides, angles and area of the triangle. The results are by no means exhaustive as such results proliferate as each new variable is added. An indication, rather than a full account, of how each formula is derived is also given, and as usual there are hints and solutions to the exercises.

1. $AZ = AY = s - a;\ BZ = BX = s - b;\ CX = CY = s - c.$
   The tangents from an external point to a circle are equal so
   $CX + AB = s.$

2. $BX_1 = BZ_1 = s - c;\ CX_1 = CY_1 = s - b;\ AZ_1 = AY_1 = s.$
   A similar argument to 1. $AZ_1 + AY_1 = AB + AC + BC = 2s,$
   but $AZ_1 = AY_1,$ *so* $BZ_1 = AZ_1 - AB = s - c.$

3. $[ABC] = rs = r_1(s - a) = r_2(s - b) = r_3(s - c).$
   Observe that $[ABC] = [IBC] + [ICA] + [IAB] =$
   $\frac{1}{2}ra + \frac{1}{2}rb + \frac{1}{2}rc$ *and that*
   $[ABC] = [I_1CA] + [I_1AB] - [I_1BC] = \frac{1}{2}r_1b + \frac{1}{2}r_1c - \frac{1}{2}r_1a.$

4. $r = a \sin \frac{1}{2}B \sin \frac{1}{2}C \sec \frac{1}{2}A.$
   Note that $a = BC = BX + XC = r \cot \frac{1}{2}B + r \cot \frac{1}{2}C.$

5. $r_1 = a \cos \frac{1}{2}B \cos \frac{1}{2}C \sec \frac{1}{2}A.$
   Observe that $a = BC = BX + XC = r_1 \tan \frac{1}{2}B + r_1 \tan \frac{1}{2}C.$

6. $AU^2 = \{bc(b + c - a)(b + c + a)\}/(b + c)^2.$
   Use $BU = ca/(b + c), UC = ba/(b + c)$ *and the cosine rule for triangles* $AUB, AUC.$

7. $AI = r\operatorname{cosec}\frac{1}{2}A$
   Consider triangle AZI

Exercises

1. Prove that $YY_1 = ZZ_1 = a$.

2. Prove that $XX_1 = |b - c|$.

3. Prove that $Z_1 Z_2 = a + b$.

4. Prove

    (a) $1/r_1 + 1/r_2 + 1/r_3 = 1/r$;

    (b) $[ABC] = \sqrt{rr_1 r_2 r_3}$;

    (c) $r_1 + r_2 + r_3 - r = 4R$.

5. Prove that I is the orthocentre of triangle $I_1 I_2 I_3$ and that H is the incentre of triangle DEF. Where are the centres of the escribed circles of triangle DEF?

6. Prove that the area of the quadrilateral $I_1 Y AZ = [ABC]$.

7. Prove that $\angle IAO = \angle HAI = \frac{1}{2}|B - C|$.

8. Prove $(AY)(YC) = [ABC]$ if and only if $\angle ABC = 90°$.

9. Prove that the pedal triangle of triangle XYZ has its sides parallel to those of triangle ABC.

10. Prove that the radius r_0 of the circle touching AB, AC and the inscribed circle is given by $r_0 = r \tan^2 \frac{1}{4}(B + C)$.

11. Prove that $I_1 X_1, I_2 X_2, I_3 X_3$ are concurrent at a point K. What point is K in relation to triangle $I_1 I_2 I_3$?

12. Prove that the area of triangle $I_1 I_2 I_3$ is equal to $2Rs$.

Theorem 3

$OI^2 = R^2 - 2Rr$ and $R \geq 2r$, with equality if and only if triangle ABC is equilateral.

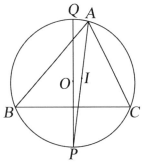

Figure 4

Proof

Let AI meet the circumcircle again at P, and draw the diameter POQ. These constructions are shown in Figure 4.

First note that $(AI)(IP) = R^2 - OI^2$, the power of I with respect to circumcircle (see Chapter 3 for the definition of the power of a point with respect to a circle).

Secondly, as has already been observed, ABC is the pedal triangle of triangle $I_1 I_2 I_3$ and I is the orthocentre of triangle $I_1 I_2 I_3$. So the circumcircle of triangle ABC is the Nine-Point Circle of triangle $I_1 I_2 I_3$ with I the external centre of similitude. It follows that $IP = PI_1$. But $\angle I_1 BI = 90^o$, so circle IBI_1 has II_1 as diameter and P as centre. This means that $PI_1 = PI = PB$ (and these are all equal to PC). Now $AI = r\operatorname{cosec}\frac{1}{2}A$ (formula 7) and since $\angle BAP = \frac{1}{2}A$ the chord $BP = 2R\sin\frac{1}{2}A$. It follows that $(AI)(IP) = (AI)(BP) = 2Rr$ and hence $OI^2 = R^2 - 2Rr$.

Since OI^2 is a non-negative quantity the inequality $R \geq 2r$ follows immediately.

Further if ABC is an equilateral triangle $r/R = \sin 30^o = \frac{1}{2}$ and finally if $R = 2r$ we have $AI = AO$ since I and O coincide. Hence $r\operatorname{cosec}\frac{1}{2}A = R = 2r$, which implies $\angle A$ is equal to 60° or 120^0. Similarly for B and C. This means $A = B = C = 60^o$ and ABC is equilateral. ∎

Theorem 4 (Feuerbach)

$IT = \frac{1}{2}R - r$ with the consequence that the incircle and the Nine-Point Circle of triangle ABC touch one another. Further the Nine-Point Circle touches each of the excircles. (This theorem provides four more interesting points on the Nine-Point Circle)

The proof of this theorem is difficult (and does not provide insight into the reasons for these remarkable results) and perhaps the best proof is by inversion. See, for example *Complex Numbers and Geometry* by Liang-Shin Hahn, *The Mathematical Association of America*, 1994.

Exercises

13. Prove that $r = 4R \sin \frac{1}{2}A \sin \frac{1}{2}B \sin \frac{1}{2}C$.

14. If a, b, c are the sides of triangle ABC and u, v, w are the angle bisectors, and u_0, v_0, w_0 are the angle bisectors extended until they are chords of the circumcircle, prove that

$$(uvwu_0v_0w_0)^{\frac{1}{2}} = abc.$$

15. Let ABC be an acute angled triangle with pedal triangle DEF. Let P be the intersection of AD and EF and Q, R the intersections of AB, AC respectively with the perpendicular bisector of PD.
    Prove that $ARDQ$ is a cyclic quadrilateral.

16. Let AI, BI, CI be extended to meet the circumcircle of triangle ABC at P, Q, R respectively. Prove that I is the orthocentre of triangle PQR.

17. ABC is a triangle and the internal bisectors of the angles at A and B meet the sides BC and CA at U and V respectively. Let CP and CQ be the perpendiculars from C to the lines BV and AU respectively. Prove that PQ is parallel to AB.

18. If x, y, z are acute angles given by the equations $\cos x = a/(b+c)$, $\cos y = b/(c+a)$, $\cos z = c/(a+b)$, prove that

$$\tan^2 \frac{1}{2}x + \tan^2 \frac{1}{2}y + \tan^2 \frac{1}{2}z = 1$$

and

$$\tan \frac{1}{2}x \tan \frac{1}{2}y \tan \frac{1}{2}z = \tan \frac{1}{2}A \tan \frac{1}{2}B \tan \frac{1}{2}C.$$

19. Prove that $OH^2 = R^2(1 - 8 \cos A \cos B \cos C)$. Hence show that
$$\cos A \cos B \cos C \le \frac{1}{8}.$$
Find an upper bound for the length of the line segment OH.

20. ABC is an acute angled triangle with pedal triangle DEF. The circle inscribed in the pedal triangle touches its sides EF, FD, DE at P, Q, R respectively. Prove that

$$QR/BC = RP/CA = PQ/AB = 2 \cos A \cos B \cos C.$$

21. Prove that $II_1^2 + I_2 I_3^2 = 16R^2$.

22. The acute angled triangle ABC and its circumcentre O are given. Triangle $A_0 B_0 C_0$ is constructed with its sides $B_0 C_0$, $C_0 A_0$, $A_0 B_0$ parallel to OA, OB, OC respectively. Prove that the line through A_0 parallel to BC, the line through B_0 parallel to CA and the line through C_0 parallel to AB meet at the incentre of triangle $A_0 B_0 C_0$.

23. In triangle ABC, I is the incentre, r the inradius and L is the midpoint of BC. LI extended meets the altitude AD at P. Prove that $AP = r$.

24. ABC is a triangle and $C = 60^o$. The internal bisectors of angles A and B meet the opposite sides in U and V respectively. Show that $AV + BU = AB$.

25. Prove that the length of the internal bisector of angle A of triangle ABC does not exceed $\frac{1}{2}(AB + AC)$.

26. A variable triangle circumscribes a fixed circle; if the circumradius is constant, find the locus of its circumcentre.

4.6   Unit 6: Hints and Solutions

1. $YY_1 = AY_1 - AY$.

2. $XX_1 = |BX_1 - BX|$.

3. $Z_1Z_2 = AZ_1 + AZ_2$.

4. For part (i) use formula 3. For part (ii) use Heron's formula and formula 3. For part (iii) again use Heron's formula and formula 3 together with the formula $4R = abc/[ABC]$.

5. For the first part note that AII_1 is a straight line and that $\angle IAI_2 = \angle IAI_3 = 90^o$. For the second part remember that the altitudes of a triangle bisect the angles of the pedal triangle. The answers to the third part are A, B and C.

6. Use the dissection

$$[I_1YAZ] = [ABC] + [I_1BC] - [YCI_1] - [ZBI_1].$$

Now observe $[I_1XC] = [YCI_1]$ since $CX = CY$ and $I_1X_1 = I_1Y_1$ and similarly $[I_1XB] = [ZBI_1]$.

7. This is an important exercise as it links the three main centres of a triangle. Let AI meet the circumcircle again at P. Then P is the midpoint of the arc BC, since $\angle BAP = \angle CAP = \frac{1}{2}A$. Now $\angle HAI = |\frac{1}{2}A - 90^o + C| = \frac{1}{2}|B - C|$. Also $\angle IAO = \angle OPI = \angle HAI$ (alternate).

8. $(AY)(YC) = \frac{1}{4}(b+c-a)(b+a-c) = \frac{1}{4}(b^2 - c^2 - a^2 + 2ac) = \frac{1}{2}ac = [ABC]$ if and only if $b^2 = c^2 + a^2$, that is if and only if $\angle ABC = 90^o$.

9. The circumcentre of triangle XYZ is the incentre of triangle ABC. The line perpendicular to BC through X therefore

passes through the circumcentre of triangle XYZ. But the lines joining the vertices of any triangle to its circumcentre are perpendicular to the sides of its pedal triangle. One of these sides is therefore parallel to BC.

10. Let I_0 be the centre of the smaller circle. Then

$$I_0 I = (r + r_0) = AI - AI_0 = (r - r_0)\operatorname{cosec} \frac{1}{2}A,$$

so

$$r_0/r = (1 - \sin \frac{1}{2}A)/(1 + \sin \frac{1}{2}A).$$

Now use $\sin \frac{1}{2}A = \cos \frac{1}{2}(B + C)$ and the double angle formulae.

11. Triangle ABC is the pedal triangle of triangle $I_1 I_2 I_3$. Now see the solution to Exercise 9. K is the circumcentre of triangle $I_1 I_2 I_3$.

12. Use the formula $[I_1 I_2 I_3] = rs + \frac{1}{2}ar_1 + \frac{1}{2}br_2 + \frac{1}{2}cr_3$ together with $r_1 a = (r_1 - a)s$ etc. You will also need, as a last step, to use $r_1 + r_2 + r_3 - r = 4R$.

13. Use formula 4 with $a = 2R \sin A = 4R \sin \frac{1}{2}A \cos \frac{1}{2}A$.

14. Use the intersecting chord theorem and formula 6 to find $uu_0 = bc$ etc.

15. P is the orthocentre of triangle AQR and hence the circumcircle of triangle AQR passes through D.

16. $\angle BQP = \angle BAP = \frac{1}{2}A$ etc.

17. $\angle AVI = \frac{1}{2}B + C$, so $\angle AIV = \frac{1}{2}(A + B)$. But

$$\angle AIC = \frac{1}{2}(A + C) + B.$$

It follows that $\angle PIC = 90^\circ - \frac{1}{2}A$. Hence $\angle PCI = \frac{1}{2}A$. This means that $\angle PQI = \frac{1}{2}A$ and since $\angle BAI = \frac{1}{2}A$ we have AB and PQ parallel (alternate).

18. Put $\tan\frac{1}{2}x = s, \tan\frac{1}{2}y = t, \tan\frac{1}{2}z = u$ and use

$$\cos x = (1 - s^2)/(1 + s^2)$$

etc. In the second part you may need Heron's formula and $\tan\frac{1}{2}A = 2r/(b + c - a)$ etc.

19. Use $OH^2 = LD^2 + (HD - OL)^2$. Equality when $A = B = C = 60^\circ$. Upper bound is $3R$.

20. The sides of the pedal triangle are $R\sin 2A, R\sin 2B, R\sin 2C$. Now use
$$DQ = DR = \frac{1}{2}(FD + DE - EF)$$
and $\angle FDE = 180^\circ - 2A$. The trigonometry in this question is somewhat laborious.

21. This is the analogue in triangle $I_1I_2I_3$, which has orthocentre I, of the relation $AH^2 + BC^2 = 4R^2$ for triangle ABC. Note that the circumcircle of triangle $I_1I_2I_3$ has radius $2R$.

22. This is an angle problem. Prove that the angles of triangle $A_0B_0C_0$ are $180^\circ - 2A, 180^\circ - 2B, 180^\circ - 2C$. Now use the fact that OB and OC make an angle $(90^\circ - A)$ with BC etc.

23. Use $AP = AD - PD$ and similar triangles to find PD in terms of IX, LX and LD, X being the point where the incircle touches BC. Express the lengths in terms of sides and angles of the triangle. Remember $AD = b\sin C = 2R\sin B\sin C$ and that $r = 4R\sin\frac{1}{2}A\sin\frac{1}{2}B\sin\frac{1}{2}C$.

24. The cosine rule for triangle ABC gives $c^2 = a^2 + b^2 - ab$. Now $BU = ca/(b+c)$ and $AV = bc/(c+a)$. The result follows easily.

25. Use formula 6. You will need to use $(b+c)^2 \geq 2bc$.

26. Let r be the radius of the inner circle and R the fixed circumradius. Let I be the centre of the inner circle, then $OI^2 = R^2 - 2Rr$, so the locus of O is a circle centre I.

4.7   Unit 7: The Simson line

Theorem 1

Let P be a point on the circumcircle of triangle ABC and L, M, N the feet of the perpendiculars from P to BC, CA, AB respectively. Then L, M, N are collinear. (Note that L, M, N are not the midpoints of the sides in this unit.)

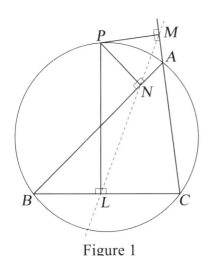

Figure 1

Proof

The method of proof is to show that $\angle MNP + \angle PNL = 180°$. $PABC$ is a cyclic quadrilateral, so

$$\angle MAP = \angle CBP.$$

$PMAN$ is a cyclic quadrilateral, so $\angle MAP = \angle MNP$. Hence

$$\angle LBP = \angle CBP = \angle MNP.$$

Now $PNLB$ is cyclic, so

$$\angle LBP + \angle PNL = 180°.$$

Therefore $\angle MNP + \angle PNL = 180°$.   ■

The converse of this theorem is that if the three perpendiculars from a point P in the plane of triangle ABC on to its sides are collinear then P lies on the circumcircle of triangle ABC. The proof is essentially the reverse of the theorem itself, the last step being the conclusion that $PABC$ is a cyclic quadrilateral. This proof is left for the reader to supply the details.

LMN is called the Simson line of P and the Simson line property generalizes to conics circumscribing triangle ABC other than the circumcircle. Details are given in Chapter 5, where an exercise is set involving the circumscribing ellipse centre G.

Exercises

1. Let the altitude AD meet the circumcircle again at D_1. Prove that the Simson line of D_1 is perpendicular to AO.

2. In Figure 1 prove that triangles PLN and PCA are similar. Hence show that

$$\frac{(PL)(MN)}{BC} = \frac{(PM)(NL)}{CA} = \frac{(PN)(LM)}{AB}.$$

3. In Figure 1 PL, PM, PN meet the circumcircle again at A_0, B_0, C_0 respectively. Prove that triangles ABC and $A_0B_0C_0$ are congruent.

4. Prove that the circumcircles of the four triangles formed by four straight lines (no two of which are parallel) have a common point.

5. In Figure 1 prove that $AB/PN = BC/PL + CA/PM$.

6. If P lies on the circumcircle of triangle ABC and H is the orthocentre, then the midpoint of PH lies on the Nine-Point Circle and on the Simson line of P.

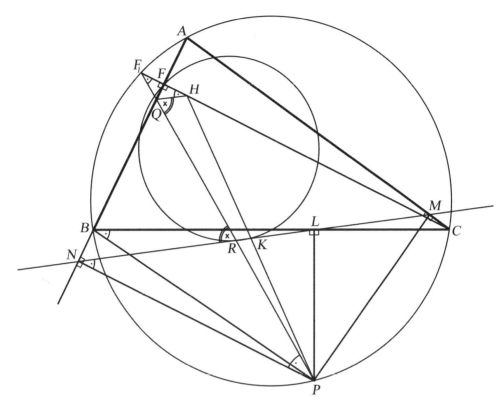

Figure 2

4.8   Unit 7: Hints and Solutions

1. $AEHF$ is cyclic, so $\angle FEH = \angle FAH$. AND_1M is cyclic so $\angle FAH = \angle D_1AN = \angle D_1MN$. But D_1M is parallel to BE. Hence MN is parallel to EF. But EF is perpendicular to AO.

2. $PNLB$ is cyclic, so $\angle PBN = \angle PLN$ (angles in the same segment). Also $PABC$ is cyclic, so $\angle PBN = \angle PBA = \angle PCA$. It follows that $\angle PLN = \angle PCA$. Now $\angle BPL = \angle BNL$ (angles in the same segment) and $\angle PNB = \angle PLB = 90°$. Since $PBCA$ is cyclic, it follows that $\angle PAC = \angle PNL$. Ratios of corresponding sides yields $PC = (PL)(CA)/LN$. Similarly triangles PCB and PMN are similar and hence $PC = (PM)(BC)/NM$. These two equations give

$$(PL)(MN)/BC = (PM)(NL)/CA$$

   and by cyclic change of letters each of these must also equal $(PN)(LM)/AB$.

3. $\angle ANM = \angle BNL = \angle BPA_0 = \angle BAA_0$ (vertically opposite and angles in the same segment). This means that AA_0 and LNM are parallel. Similarly BB_0 and CC_0 are also parallel to the Simson line of P.

4. Let P be the point of intersection of any two circumcircles. The Simson lines of P with respect to the corresponding triangles coincide, since they share two points. Now take one of the other triangles. Perpendiculars from its sides meet at P which therefore lies on its circumcircle by the converse of Theorem 1.

5. Since $LM = LN + NM$ we have $[PML] = [PNL] + [PNM]$. Now $[PML] = \frac{1}{2}(PM)(PL)\sin C = \{(PM)(PL)(AB)\}/4R$.

Similar results for $[PNL]$ and $[PNM]$ give

$$(PM)(PL)(AB) = (PN)(PL)(BC) + (PL)(PN)(CA)$$

from which the result follows.

6. Use Figure 2. The angles marked with a dot should be proved equal using cyclic quadrilaterals and the known fact that $HF = FF_1$. It follows that $RN = RP$. Now R is therefore the centre of the circle QNP and hence $RN = RQ = RP$. Next the angles marked with a cross are equal. QH and NR are therefore parallel (alternate). Now

$$PR : PQ = PK : PH = 1 : 2.$$

So RK is parallel to QH also. Thus NRK is a straight line and K lies on NLM.

Chapter 5

Areal co-ordinates, Ceva and Menelaus

5.1 Unit 8: Elementary vector treatment of a straight line and plane with a triangle

Introduction

This chapter is concerned with the application of vectors and co-ordinates to lines and planes with particular reference to triangles. It enables a number of more advanced theorems on the triangle to be proved and provides the student with an additional choice of approach to problems on triangles and circles (and conics), other than pure geometry and trigonometry.

In order to reach the point where geometrical applications can be made, it is necessary to cover some basic results of vector theory, leading to the introduction of **areal** (or **barycentric**) co-ordinates which provide a very powerful tool for dealing with the geometry of the triangle. Although the co-ordinate system is first reached by means of ratios of lengths and areas, it turns out to be possible to find a metric in the plane of the triangle, enabling distances and angles to be calculated.

Part of the skill of dealing with problems in geometry is choice of method and on this question no absolute guidance can be given. There is a subjective element involved. Some students will search for a pure geometrical approach before resorting to co-ordinates; others will use co-ordinates if their use appears straightforward enough. But what is straightforward to some may not be so to others, as co-ordinate methods often involve a high degree of algebraic skill, whereas pure geometrical methods often involve a degree of spatial perception that not everyone possesses.

Vector treatment of the line

Theorem 1 (Section theorem - 1st formulation)

Let BC be a line through distinct points B and C, and let O be a point not on BC. Write $\mathbf{OB} = \mathbf{b}$ and $\mathbf{OC} = \mathbf{c}$. Then a point P for which $\mathbf{OP} = \mathbf{p}$, lies on BC if and only if constants y and z can be found such that $\mathbf{p} = y\mathbf{b} + z\mathbf{c}$ and $y + z = 1$.

(Note that $\mathbf{b}, \mathbf{c}$, in the vector context, have nothing to do with the side lengths CA, AB. In general we use a small bold letter, such as $\mathbf{p}$ to represent the vector position of P relative to an origin O.)

Proof
First, if P lies on BC, then there exists a constant t such that $\mathbf{OP} = \mathbf{OB} + t\mathbf{BC} = \mathbf{b} + t(\mathbf{c} - \mathbf{b}) = (1 - t)\mathbf{b} + t\mathbf{c}$ and with $y = 1 - t$ and $z = t$, we have $y + z = 1$. The converse is immediate from reading the sequence of equations in reverse. ∎

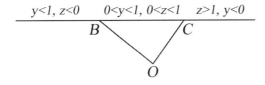

Figure 1

The ordered pair (y, z) with $y + z = 1$ may be thought of as co-ordinates of a point on the line. B is $(1, 0)$ and C is $(0, 1)$. See Figure 1 for how y and z alter along the line.

We use the sign convention in which PQ is positive if Q is to the right of P and PQ is negative if Q is to the left of P.

For example, if $z_1 = \frac{2}{5}$ and $y_1 = \frac{3}{5}$, we have $\frac{z_1}{y_1} = \frac{2}{3}$ and P_1

divides BC internally in the ratio 2:3. We have

$$\mathbf{p_1} = \frac{3}{5}\mathbf{b} + \frac{2}{5}\mathbf{c} \text{ and } \frac{BP_1}{P_1C} = \frac{2}{3}.$$

See Figure 2.

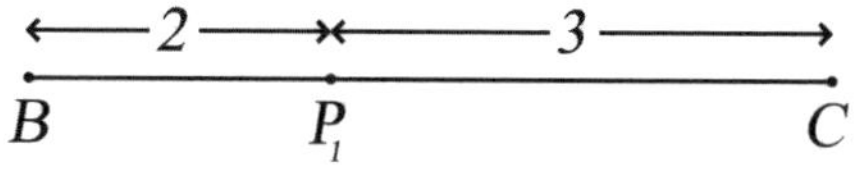

Figure 2

But if $z_2 = -2$ and $y_2 = 3$, $\frac{z_2}{y_2} = \frac{-2}{3}$ and P_2 divides BC externally in the ratio 2:3. We have

$$\mathbf{p_2} = 3\mathbf{b} - 2\mathbf{c} \text{ and } \frac{BP_2}{P_2C} = \frac{-2}{3}.$$

See Figure 3.

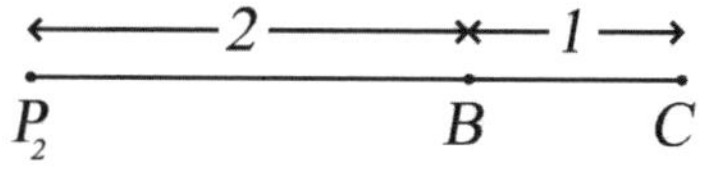

Figure 3

Exercise

1. Write down the vector $\mathbf{p}$ in terms of $\mathbf{b}$ and $\mathbf{c}$ in the following cases:

   (i) P divides BC internally in the ratio 4:1;

(ii) P divides BC externally in the ratio 4:1;

(iii) P divides BC internally in the ratio 2:1;

(iv) P divides BC externally in the ratio 1:2.

Theorem 2 (Section theorem – 2nd formulation) The points A, B, C with vector positions $\mathbf{a}, \mathbf{b}, \mathbf{c}$ are collinear if and only if constants x, y, z not all zero exist such that $x + y + z = 0$ and $x\mathbf{a} + y\mathbf{b} + z\mathbf{c} = \mathbf{0}$.

Proof

For the sufficiency, one of the constants, say x, is non-zero so we can divide by it giving

$$\mathbf{a} = \frac{y}{(y+z)}\mathbf{b} + \frac{z}{(y+z)}\mathbf{c}$$

and $\frac{y}{(y+z)} + \frac{z}{(y+z)} = 1$.

For the necessity, if $\mathbf{a} = y_0\mathbf{b} + z_0\mathbf{c}$ with $y_0 + z_0 = 1$, then $x + y + z = 1 - y_0 - z_0 = 0$. ∎

Vector treatment of the plane of a triangle

Theorem 3

Let A, B, C be the vertices of a non-degenerate triangle, with position vectors $\mathbf{a}, \mathbf{b}, \mathbf{c}$, relative to an origin O not lying in the plane S of ABC, then for every point P in S there exist unique co-ordinates x, y, z such that $\mathbf{OP} = x\mathbf{a} + y\mathbf{b} + z\mathbf{c}$ and $x + y + z = 1$.

Proof

Using oblique axes AB, AC in S we have $\mathbf{OP} = \mathbf{OA} + y\mathbf{AB} + z\mathbf{AC}$, for some values of y and z and this is equal to $(1 - y - z)\mathbf{a} + y\mathbf{b} + z\mathbf{c}$. Now define $x = 1 - y - z$. Uniqueness follows from the linear independence of $\mathbf{a}, \mathbf{b}, \mathbf{c}$ ∎

Theorem 4

The result of Theorem 3 is still valid even if O lies in the plane S.

Proof

It is only the uniqueness that requires proof, the rest of the algebra being identical. Suppose then we have $x\mathbf{a} + y\mathbf{b} + z\mathbf{c} = x_0\mathbf{a} + y_0\mathbf{b} + z_0\mathbf{c}$ with $x + y + z = 1$ and $x_0 + y_0 + z_0 = 1$, then $(x - x_0)\mathbf{a} + (y - y_0)\mathbf{b} + (z - z_0)\mathbf{c} = 0$. It follows from Theorem 2, since A, B, C are not collinear, that $x = x_0, y = y_0, z = z_0$.   ∎

Theorem 5

The co-ordinates (x, y, z) with $x + y + z = 1$ are invariant under change of origin.

Proof

Suppose we move the origin from O to O_1 where $\mathbf{OO_1} = \mathbf{t}$. Define $\mathbf{O_1A} = \mathbf{a_1}, \mathbf{O_1B} = \mathbf{b_1}, \mathbf{O_1C} = \mathbf{c_1}$. Now $\mathbf{O_1P} = \mathbf{OP} - \mathbf{t}$ and hence $\mathbf{O_1P} = x\mathbf{a} + y\mathbf{b} + z\mathbf{c} - (x + y + z)\mathbf{t} = x\mathbf{a_1} + y\mathbf{b_1} + z\mathbf{c_1}$.   ∎

The consequence of these theorems is that we may think of (x, y, z) as the co-ordinates of P, that they reflect the position of P relative to triangle ABC rather than to some particular origin. Such co-ordinates are called **areal** or **barycentric co-ordinates**. The reason for the word 'areal' appears shortly.

Exercises

2. Write down the areal co-ordinates of A, B, C, L, M, N and the centroid G.

3. Let ABC be a triangle with P, Q, R lying on BC, CA, AB respectively such that $\frac{BP}{PC} = \frac{5}{6}, \frac{CQ}{QA} = \frac{3}{5}, \frac{AR}{RB} = \frac{2}{1}$. Prove that the lines AP, BQ, CR are concurrent at a point K and determine the areal co-ordinates of K.

4. Let $A(1, 0, 0); B(0, 1, 0); C(0, 0, 1); A'(2, 0, 0); B'(0, 3, 0);$ $C'(0, 0, 5)$. Suppose AB meets $A'B'$ at N, with L and M similarly defined. Prove that L, M, N are collinear.

5. Let ABC be a triangle serving as reference for areal co-ordinates of points. Locate the position of the point P in the plane with areal co-ordinates $(4, -1, -2)$ by finding the areal co-ordinates of U, V, W the intersections of AP with BC, BP with CA, CP with AB respectively.

Areas using vectors and areal co-ordinates.

As is well known the area of triangle PQR in terms of the position vectors $\mathbf{p}, \mathbf{q}, \mathbf{r}$ is given by $[PQR]\mathbf{n} = \frac{1}{2}(\mathbf{q} - \mathbf{p}) \times (\mathbf{r} - \mathbf{p}) = \frac{1}{2}(\mathbf{p} \times \mathbf{q} + \mathbf{q} \times \mathbf{r} + \mathbf{r} \times \mathbf{p})$. Here $\mathbf{n}$ is the unit normal perpendicular to PQR, with the convention that $[PQR]$ is positive if the letters P, Q, R appear in anticlockwise order around the triangle.

Theorem 6

Let the areal co-ordinates of a point P in the plane of ABC be (x, y, z) then

$$x = \frac{[PBC]}{[ABC]}, y = \frac{[PCA]}{[ABC]}, z = \frac{[PAB]}{[ABC]}.$$

Proof

We know from above that $[ABC]\mathbf{n} = \frac{1}{2}(\mathbf{a} \times \mathbf{b} + \mathbf{b} \times \mathbf{c} + \mathbf{c} \times \mathbf{a})$. Also

$$[PBC]\mathbf{n} = \frac{1}{2}\mathbf{BC} \times \mathbf{BP} = \frac{1}{2}(\mathbf{c} - \mathbf{b}) \times (x\mathbf{a} + (y-1)\mathbf{b} + z\mathbf{c}) = x[ABC]\mathbf{n}$$

since $1 - y - z = x$. Similarly for y and z. ∎

The property embodied by Theorem 6 explains why the co-ordinates are called **areal** co-ordinates. The uniqueness property is easier to understand now that the geometrical meaning of the co-ordinates has been demonstrated. No other geometrical identification is possible.

Note the importance of the sign convention. If $x = 0$ then P lies on BC. If $x > 0$ then PBC is anticlockwise, which means that P is on the same side of BC as A. Whereas if $x < 0$ then PBC is clockwise, which means that P is on the other side of BC than A. See Figure 4.

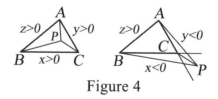

Figure 4

The advantage of areal co-ordinates is that there are three of them, which means that symmetry of form is maintained in dealing with problems involving a triangle. Also the uniqueness of (x, y, z) subject to $x + y + z = 1$ means that vectors $\mathbf{a}$, $\mathbf{b}$, $\mathbf{c}$ may be used as if they are independent, even when they are not. (Compare Theorems 3 and 4.)

Exercise

6. P and Q are distinct points having areal co-ordinates (x, y, z) and (x_0, y_0, z_0) respectively. Find the areal co-ordinates of the point where PQ meets BC. What is the condition that PQ is parallel to BC?

Theorem 7

Let P_k have co-ordinates $(x_k, y_k, z_k), k = 1$ to 3, then the area of triangle $P_1 P_2 P_3$ is given by

$$[P_1 P_2 P_3] = \det \begin{pmatrix} x_1 & x_2 & x_3 \\ y_1 & y_2 & y_3 \\ z_1 & z_2 & z_3 \end{pmatrix} [ABC].$$

Proof

Since they are all equal we need only calculate the first co-ordinate of the vector product $\mathbf{P_2 P_3} \times \mathbf{P_2 P_1}$. This is

$$(y_3 - y_2)(z_1 - z_2) - (z_3 - z_2)(y_1 - y_2).$$

That this equals the above determinant is a matter of straightforward algebra, using $x_k = 1 - y_k - z_k$.
It is a lengthy calculation, but not difficult, and the details are left to the reader. ■

As a corollary to Theorem 7 one can introduce current co-ordinates (x, y, z) and the equation of $P_2 P_3$ is then

$$\det \begin{pmatrix} x & x_2 & x_3 \\ y & y_2 & y_3 \\ z & z_2 & z_3 \end{pmatrix} = 0.$$

This is because the area enclosed by three points on a line is zero. Written out in full this becomes

$$(y_2 z_3 - y_3 z_2)x + (z_2 x_3 - z_3 x_2)y + (x_2 y_3 - x_3 y_2)z = 0.$$

You may have solved Exercise 6 by using vectors. If so you will find it instructive to solve it again by writing down the equation of PQ using current co-ordinates and finding where it meets the line with equation $x = 0$, which is the equation of BC.

Note that the coefficient of x in the last equation is equal to $[AP_2 P_3]$, the coefficient of y is $[BP_2 P_3]$ and the coefficient of z is $[CP_2 P_3]$. Since the three triangles concerned have a common base $P_2 P_3$ it follows that their areas are proportional to their heights (with due regard to sign). We therefore have the following theorem:

Theorem 8

For the line with equation $px+qy+rz = 0$, the signed perpendicular distances from A, B, C on to the line are proportional to p, q, r respectively.

Theorem 9

The condition for parallelism for the two (non-identical) lines with equations $p_1 x + q_1 y + r_1 z = 0$ and $p_2 x + q_2 y + r_2 z = 0$ is

$$\det \begin{pmatrix} p_1 & q_1 & r_1 \\ p_2 & q_2 & r_2 \\ 1 & 1 & 1 \end{pmatrix} = 0.$$

Proof

The two equations given always have a solution but this fails to correspond to a real point if the solution satisfies $x + y + z = 0$. This corresponds to the vanishing of the determinant, and since two lines fail to meet only when they are parallel the result follows. ■

Expanded out the condition for parallel lines is

$$p_1(q_2 - r_2) + q_1(r_2 - p_2) + r_1(p_2 - q_2) = 0.$$

In order to illustrate the technique of using current co-ordinates we provide a worked example.

Worked Example

ABC is a triangle and L is the midpoint of BC. Q lies on AL and CQ meets AB (possibly extended) at P. Prove that

$$\frac{PQ}{QC} = \frac{AP}{AB}.$$

$A(1,0,0)$ and $L(0, \frac{1}{2}, \frac{1}{2})$ so the co-ordinates of Q may be written as $Q(1-t, \frac{t}{2}, \frac{t}{2})$. $C(0,0,1)$, so the equation of CQ is

$$\frac{-tx}{2} + (1-t)y = 0.$$

This meets AB, $z = 0$, at the point $P(\frac{2(1-t)}{(2-t)}, \frac{t}{(2-t)}, 0)$. It follows that $\frac{AP}{AB} = \frac{t}{(2-t)}$ where t is not equal to 2. Furthermore

$$\mathbf{q} = \frac{t}{2}\mathbf{c} + (1 - \frac{t}{2})\mathbf{p}.$$

Hence, by the section theorem, we have $\frac{PQ}{QC} = \frac{t}{(2-t)}$ also. (The exceptional point $t = 2$ corresponds to when $AL = LQ$ and then CQ is parallel to AB.)

Exercises

7. What can be said about the location of $K(x, y, z)$ when

    (i) $x = 0$;

    (ii) $y = 0$;

    (iii) $z = 0$;

    (iv) $x + y = 0$;

    (v) $y + z = 0$;

    (vi) $z + x = 0$?

8. Verify, by working out appropriate areas, that the areal co-ordinates of key points in the triangle are as follows:

(a) I, the incentre: $\dfrac{(a, b, c)}{(a + b + c)}$;

(b) I_1, the excentre opposite A: $\dfrac{(-a, b, c)}{(b + c - a)}$;

(c) I_2, the excentre opposite B: $\dfrac{(a, -b, c)}{(c + a - b)}$;

(d) I_3, the excentre opposite C: $\dfrac{(a, b, -c)}{(a + b - c)}$;

(e) O, the circumcentre: $\dfrac{(\sin 2A, \sin 2B, \sin 2C)}{4 \sin A \sin B \sin C}$;

(f) G, the centroid: $(\frac{1}{3}, \frac{1}{3}, \frac{1}{3})$;

(g) H, the orthocentre: $\dfrac{(\tan A, \tan B, \tan C)}{(\tan A + \tan B + \tan C)}$;

alternatively $(\cot B \cot C, \cot C \cot A, \cot A \cot B)$;

(h) T, the nine-point centre:

$$\frac{(\sin 2B + \sin 2C, \sin 2C + \sin 2A, \sin 2A + \sin 2B)}{8 \sin A \sin B \sin C}.$$

The complicated forms for O, H and T mean that areal co-ordinates methods are less suitable for problems involving these points.

5.2 Unit 8: Hints and Solutions

1. (i) $\mathbf{p} = \frac{1}{5}\mathbf{b} + \frac{4}{5}\mathbf{c}$;

    (ii) $\mathbf{p} = -\frac{1}{3}\mathbf{b} + \frac{4}{3}\mathbf{c}$;

    (iii) $\mathbf{p} = \frac{2}{3}\mathbf{b} + \frac{1}{3}\mathbf{c}$;

    (iv) $\mathbf{p} = 2\mathbf{b} - \mathbf{c}$.

    Note the coefficients add up to 1 and if the point P is nearer B than C, then the coefficient of $\mathbf{b}$ is greater than the coefficient of $\mathbf{c}$, and vice versa.

2. $A(1,0,0); B(0,1,0); C(0,0,1); L(0,\frac{1}{2},\frac{1}{2}); M(\frac{1}{2},0,\frac{1}{2}); N(\frac{1}{2},\frac{1}{2},0);$ $G(\frac{1}{3},\frac{1}{3},\frac{1}{3})$.

3. $P(0,\frac{6}{11},\frac{5}{11})$; points on AP have co-ordinates $(1-t,\frac{6t}{11},\frac{5t}{11})$, where t is a parameter. Similar expressions may be written down for points on BQ and CR. The point $K(\frac{3}{14},\frac{6}{14},\frac{5}{14})$ lies on all three lines.

4. You should find $L(0,6,-5); M(\frac{8}{3},0,-\frac{5}{3}); N(4,-3,0)$ and $\mathbf{m} = \frac{1}{3}(2\mathbf{n}+\mathbf{l})$ so that M divides LN internally in the ratio 2:1.

5. $U(0,\frac{1}{3},\frac{2}{3}); V(2,0,-1); W(\frac{4}{3},-\frac{1}{3},0)$.

6. $\left(0, \dfrac{(yx_0 - xy_0)}{(x_0 - x)}, \dfrac{(zx_0 - xz_0)}{(x_0 - x)}\right)$. If $x = x_0$ then PQ is parallel to BC.

7. (i) K lies on BC;

    (ii) K lies on CA;

    (iii) K lies on AB;

    (iv) K lies on a line parallel to AB through C;

    (v) K lies on a line parallel to BC through A.

(vi) K lies on a line parallel to AC through B.

8. $[IBC] = \frac{1}{2}ra$, so the co-ordinates are proportional to a, b, c; $[I_1BC] = -\frac{1}{2}r_1a, [I_1CA] = \frac{1}{2}r_1b$ etc., so the co-ordinates are proportional to $-a, b, c$. Similar working holds for I_2 and I_3. $[OBC] = \frac{1}{2}(2R\sin A)(R\cos A)$, so the co-ordinates are prportional to $\sin 2A, \sin 2B, \sin 2C$. Note that

$$\sin 2A + \sin 2B + \sin 2C = 4\sin A \sin B \sin C.$$

Now

$$[HBC] = \frac{1}{2}(2R\sin A)(2R\cos B \cos C),$$

so that the co-ordinates are proportional to $\tan A$, $\tan B$, $\tan C$ or

$$\cot B \cot C, \ \cot C \cot A, \ \cot A \cot B.$$

Note that the co-ordinates of the alternative form sum to 1. For T use $\mathbf{OT} = \mathbf{TH}$.

5.3   Unit 9: Ceva's Theorem

All line segments in this unit contain, when appropriate, a sign as well as a magnitude.

Theorem 1 (Ceva)

If ABC is a triangle and P, Q, R lie on BC, CA, AB (possibly extended) respectively, then AP, BQ, CR are concurrent at a point K if and only if constants l, m, n exist such that none of l, m, n, $m + n, n + l, l + m, l + m + n$ is zero and

$$\frac{BP}{PC} = \frac{n}{m}, \frac{CQ}{QA} = \frac{l}{n}, \frac{AR}{RB} = \frac{m}{l}.$$

Proof
Sufficiency

If $\frac{BP}{PC} = \frac{n}{m}$ then P has co-ordinates $(0, \frac{m}{m+n}, \frac{n}{m+n})$ a point that is well defined since $(m + n)$ is not zero, and does not coincide with B or C since m, n are not zero. The point K with co-ordinates $(\frac{l}{(l+m+n)}, \frac{m}{(l+m+n)}, \frac{n}{(l+m+n)})$ is well defined, since $l+m+n$ is nonzero; nor does it lie on any of the sides of the triangle since none of l, m, n is zero. Furthermore its vector position

$$\mathbf{k} = \frac{l}{(l + m + n)}\mathbf{a} + \frac{(m + n)}{(l + m + n)}\mathbf{p},$$

so K lies on AP. In fact $\frac{AK}{KP} = \frac{(m+n)}{l}$ (by the first form of the section theorem). By cyclic change of l, m, n it follows that K also lies on BQ and CR, so the lines AP, BQ, CR are concurrent.

(Note that there are seven possible regions internal and external in which K may lie, since one, two or three of l, m, n are positive. A pure geometrical proof of Ceva's theorem, requires separate consideration for each of these possibilities. The advantage of the carefully established sign convention that has been put in place involving directed line segments, is that the same algebraic proof suffices for all seven cases at once.)

Necessity

If K is a point not on AB, BC, CA then it will have a set of areal co-ordinates, say (l, m, n), where $l + m + n = 1$ (and is therefore non-zero) and l, m, n are not zero. We also exclude cases with $l + m = 0, n = 1$ (and so on by cyclic change) to avoid cases in which KC is parallel to AB (and so on by cyclic change). Then the point P with position vector $\mathbf{p}$ defined by

$$\mathbf{p} = \frac{(l + m + n)}{(m + n)}\mathbf{k} - \frac{l}{(m + n)}\mathbf{a}$$

has co-ordinates $(0, \frac{m}{(m+n)}, \frac{n}{(m+n)})$ and so $\frac{BP}{PC} = \frac{n}{m}$. Similarly by cyclic change $\frac{CQ}{QA} = \frac{l}{n}$ and $\frac{AR}{RB} = \frac{m}{l}$. ∎

A possible misunderstanding in connection with Ceva's theorem is to suppose that if P, Q, R are points on BC, CA, AB such that $(BP)(CQ)(AR) = (PC)(QA)(RB)$ then AP, BQ, CR are concurrent. In fact if $l + m + n = 0$ then the three lines are parallel. For example if P is the midpoint of BC, Q divides CA externally in the ratio 3:1 and R divides AB externally in the ratio 2:3, then $3\mathbf{AP} = 2\mathbf{QB} = \mathbf{RC}$. In problem solving it is necessary to be on the look out for singular cases.

Exercises

1. Use Ceva's theorem to prove that the internal bisectors of the angles of a triangle are concurrent.

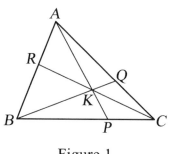

Figure 1

2. Prove that in the figure for Ceva's theorem (Figure 1)

$$\frac{KP}{AP} + \frac{KQ}{BQ} + \frac{KR}{CR} = 1.$$

3. Prove that in figures for Ceva's theorem

(i) $\dfrac{[ARQ]}{[ABC]} = \dfrac{mn}{\{(l+m)(l+n)\}}$

(ii) $\dfrac{[PQR]}{[ABC]} = \dfrac{2lmn}{\{(l+m)(m+n)(n+l)\}}$

What is the maximum area of triangle PQR given triangle ABC as K varies over all points interior to triangle ABC?

4. Prove that in figures for Ceva's theorem, if L, M, N are the midpoints of BC, CA, AB and lines are drawn through L, M, N parallel to AP, BQ, CR respectively, then these lines are concurrent.

5. Let P, Q, R lie on BC, CA, AB respectively and suppose AP, BQ, CR are concurrent. Let the circle PQR cut BC, CA, AB at P_0, Q_0, R_0 respectively. Prove that AP_0, BQ_0, CR_0 are concurrent or parallel.

6. Use Ceva's theorem to provide another proof that the altitudes of a triangle are concurrent.

7. Use areal co-ordinates to illustrate that the internal bisector of angle BAC and the external bisectors of angles CBA and ACB are concurrent at I_1, the centre of the escribed circle opposite A.

8. Find the areal co-ordinates of J, the centre of mass of a uniform wire framework in the shape of triangle ABC.

   (i) Prove that I, J, G are collinear and that $IG : GJ = 2 : 1$.

   (ii) Show that the lines through L, M, N parallel to the angle bisectors AU, BV, CW respectively concur at J.

   (iii) Prove that the triangles IGH and JGO are similar.

9. Let the incircle touch the sides BC, CA, AB at X, Y, Z respectively. Prove that AX, BY, CZ are concurrent at W_0, **Gergonne's Point**, whose unnormalized areal co-ordinates are given by

$$((a-b+c)(a+b-c), (b-c+a)(b+c-a), (c-a+b)(c+a-b)).$$

10. Let the escribed circle opposite A touch BC at X_1, with Y_2 and Z_3 similarly defined. Prove that AX_1, BY_2, CZ_3 are concurrent at W, **Nagel's point**, whose areal co-ordinates are

$$((b + c - a), (c + a - b), (a + b - c))/(a + b + c).$$

Deduce that W lies on the line IGJ and that J is the midpoint of IW. Conclude that W and G are respectively the external and internal centres of similitude of the incircles of triangles ABC and LMN.

11. Prove that $OW = R - 2r$ and that $WH^2 = 4(R^2 - 2Rr)$.

12. L, M, N are the midpoints of BC, CA, AB. Let P, Q, R lie on BC, CA, AB respectively and be such that AP, BQ, CR are concurrent. The midpoints of AP, BQ, CR are denoted by P_0, Q_0, R_0 respectively. Prove that LP_0, MQ_0, NR_0 are concurrent.

5.4   Unit 9: Hints and Solutions

1. By the sine rule on triangles ABP and ACP we find $\frac{BP}{PC} = \frac{c}{b}$ etc., by cyclic change. And $\left(\frac{c}{b}\right)\left(\frac{a}{c}\right)\left(\frac{b}{a}\right) = 1$. a, b, c are all positive so this is a case of concurrence at an internal point I with co-ordinates $\frac{(a,b,c)}{a+b+c}$.

2. $\frac{KP}{AP} = \frac{l}{(l+m+n)}$ etc. (see the proof of Ceva's theorem).

3. For (i) and (ii) you need co-ordinates of P, Q, R. For example for P one has $P\frac{(0,m,n)}{(m+n)}$. Then use the formula for area given in Theorem 7 of Unit 8. The maximum value of $[PQR]$ is $\frac{1}{4}[ABC]$ when K is at the centroid G. The easiest way to prove this is to use the Arithmetic mean/Geometric mean inequality first establishing $(l+m+n)(lm+mn+nl) \geq 9lmn$ from which the required inequality $(l+m)(m+n)(n+1) \geq 8lmn$ follows quickly.

4. The centroid G is the internal centre of similitude of triangles ABC and LMN, scale factor $\frac{1}{2}$. Under this transformation the point $K(l, m, n)$ is transformed into a point with co-ordinates $\left(\frac{1}{3} - \frac{1}{2}(l - \frac{1}{3}), \frac{1}{3} - \frac{1}{2}(m - \frac{1}{3}), \frac{1}{3} - \frac{1}{2}(n - \frac{1}{3})\right) = \left(\frac{1}{2} - \frac{1}{2}l, \frac{1}{2} - \frac{1}{2}m, \frac{1}{2} - \frac{1}{2}n\right)$. This is the point of concurrence of the three lines given, for what happens in triangle ABC also happens in triangle LMN, in view of the line through L being parallel to AK.

5. By the intersecting chord theorem we have

$$(BP)(BP_0) = (BR)(BR_0), (CQ)(CQ_0) = (CP)(CP_0),$$

and $(AR)(AR_0) = (AQ)(AQ_0)$. By Ceva's theorem we also have

$$(BP)(CQ)(AR) = (PC)(QA)(RB).$$

It follows that

$$(BP_0)(CQ_0)(AR_0) = (P_0C)(Q_0A)(R_0B)$$

and hence by the converse of Ceva's theorem (and the remark following the proof) AP_0, BQ_0, CR_0 are concurrent or parallel.

6. Use $BD = c\cos B, CE = a\cos C$ etc. Some thought should be given to the use of the sign convention in the case when one of the angles is obtuse.

7. The areal co-ordinates of I_1 are $(-a, b, c)/(b + c - a)$. AI_1 bisects BC internally in the ratio $c : b$, but BI_1 bisects CA externally in the ratio $a : c$. Hence the significance of the minus sign.

8. Replace the sides with masses proportional to their lengths at their midpoints. You should find J has co-ordinates

$$(b + c, c + a, a + b)\{2(a + b + c)\}.$$

    (i) Since I has co-ordinates $(a, b, c)/(a+b+c)$, it is evident that $\mathbf{g} = \frac{1}{3}(\mathbf{i} + 2\mathbf{j})$ This means that $IG : GJ = 2 : 1$.

    (ii) See Exercise 4, with K replaced by I.

    (iii) Compare the line IGJ with the Euler line HGO.

9. $\frac{BX}{XC} = \frac{(s-b)}{(s-c)}$, so X is the point $(0, a + b - c, a - b + c)/2a$. The equation of AX is therefore $(a - b + c)y = (a + b - c)z$. Evidently W_0 lies on this line. By cyclic change of letters it follows that BY and CZ also pass through W_0.

10. $\frac{BX_1}{X_1C} = (s - c)/(s - b)$, so the co-ordinates of X_1 are $(0, (c+a-b), (a+b-c))/2a$. The equation of AX_1 is therfore

$(a + b - c)y = (c + a - b)z$. Evidently W lies on this line. By cyclic change of letters it follows that BY_2 and CZ_3 also pass through W. Next check that $\mathbf{j} = \frac{1}{2}(\mathbf{i} + \mathbf{w})$. For the final part note that the relative disposition of points I, G, J, W on this line is exactly the same as O, G, T, H on the Euler line. You also need to check that J is the incentre of triangle LMN.

11. Draw a diagram of the two lines $OGTH$ and $IGJW$. You will find that OW is twice the length of IT, which from Feuerbach's theorem is known to be $\frac{1}{2}(R - 2r)$. Likewise $WH = 2OI$.

12. Let the point of concurrence of AP, BQ, CR have co-ordinates (x, y, z). Then P has co-ordinates $(0, y, z)/(y + z)$, and P_0 has co-ordinates $(y + z, y, z)/2(y + z)$. In terms of the vector positions of M and N, the vector position of P_0 is therefore $(z\mathbf{m} + y\mathbf{n})/(y + z)$. Now use LMN as triangle of reference. L has co-ordinates $(1, 0, 0)$ and P_0 lies on MN with co-ordinates $(0, z, y)/(y + z)$. It follows that the point of concurrence of LP_0, MQ_0, NR_0 has co-ordinates proportional to $(1/l, 1/m, 1/n)$.

5.5   Unit 10: Menelaus's Theorem

All line segments in this unit contain, where appropriate, a sign as well as a magnitude.

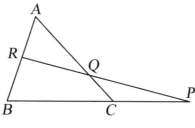

Figure 1

Theorem 1 (Menelaus)

If ABC is a triangle and P, Q, R lie on BC, CA, AB respectively, then P, Q, R are collinear if and only if there exist constants l, m, n such that none of $l, m, n, m - n, n + l, l + m$ is zero and

$$BP/PC = n/(-m), \quad CQ/QA = l/n, \quad AR/RB = m/l.$$

Proof

Sufficiency
With ratios as stated the vector positions of P, Q, R are

$$
\begin{aligned}
\mathbf{p} &= (-m\mathbf{b} + n\mathbf{c})/(n - m), \\
\mathbf{q} &= (l\mathbf{a} + n\mathbf{c})/(n + l), \\
\mathbf{r} &= (l\mathbf{a} + m\mathbf{b})/(l + m).
\end{aligned}
$$

Observe now that $(n - m)\mathbf{p} - (n + l)\mathbf{q} + (l + m)\mathbf{r} = \mathbf{0}$ and $(n - m) - (n + l) + (l + m) = 0$, so by the second form of the section theorem P, Q, R are collinear.

Necessity

If P, Q, R are collinear then by the second form of the section theorem there exist constants x, y, z, not all zero such that $x + y + z = 0$ and $x\mathbf{p} + y\mathbf{q} + z\mathbf{r} = \mathbf{0}$. P lies on BC so there exists a constant s, not equal to 0 or 1, such that $\mathbf{p} = (1 - s)\mathbf{b} + s\mathbf{c}$. Similarly t and u exist such that $\mathbf{q} = (1 - t)\mathbf{c} + t\mathbf{a}, \mathbf{r} = (1 - u)\mathbf{a} + u\mathbf{b}$. Hence we have $x(1 - s)\mathbf{b} + xs\mathbf{c} + y(1 - t)\mathbf{c} + yt\mathbf{a} - (x + y)(1 - u)\mathbf{a} - (x + y)u\mathbf{b} = \mathbf{0}$. Equating coefficients we get $yt = (x + y)(1 - u), x(1 - s) = (x + y)u, xs = -y(1 - t)$. Eliminating x, y we obtain $(1 - s)(1 - t)(1 - u) = -stu$. Setting $s/(1 - s) = n/(-m), t/(1 - t) = l/n$, it follows that $u/(1 - u) = m/l$. But $BP/PC = s/(1 - s), CQ/QA = t/(1 - t), AR/RB = u/(1 - u)$ and the result follows.

There are several possible figures, corresponding to different signs of l, m, n. Figure 1 corresponds to the case in which l, m, n are all positive. The algebra is valid for all cases. ∎

Exercises

1. Let the external bisector of $\angle BAC$ meet BC at X_0, with Y_0, Z_0 on CA, AB respectively similarly defined. Prove that X_0, Y_0, Z_0 are collinear.

2. K is a point in the interior of triangle ABC. Prove that the external bisectors of the angles AKB, BKC, CKA meet AB, BC, CA respectively in three collinear points.

3. In triangle ABC, I is the incentre and I_1 is the centre of the escribed circle opposite A. II_1 meets BC at U. A given straight line through U meets AB, AC at V, W respectively. IV, I_1W intersect at P. IW, I_1V intersect at Q. Prove that PAQ is a straight line perpendicular to II_1.

Theorem 2 (Desargues)

Let ABC and UVW be two triangles in which AU, BV, CW meet at a point K (such triangles are said to be in perspective). Let BC meet VW at P, CA meet WU at Q and AB meet UV at R; then P, Q, R are collinear.

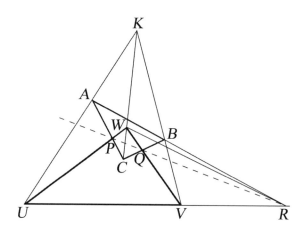

Figure 2

Proof

Consider the transversal VPW of triangle BKC. By Menelaus's theorem we have $(BP)(CW)(KV) = -(PC)(WK)(VB)$. Two similar relations hold by cyclic change of letters A, B, C and U, V, W. It follows that $(BP)(CQ)(AR) = -(PC)(QA)(RB)$. By the converse of Menelaus's theorem it now follows that PQR is a transversal of triangle ABC and hence that P, Q, R are collinear. ■

The theorem may also be proved by standard two dimensional vector analysis using K as origin.

Exercises

4. Prove that if triangles XYZ and UVW have their corresponding sides parallel, then either XU, YV, ZW are parallel or concurrent.

5. State and prove the converse of Desargues's theorem.

6. A circle S_3 touches externally two circles S_1 and S_2, centres A, B at C, D respectively. A circle S_4 of different radius from S_3 also touches S_1 and S_2 externally at E, F. Prove that AB, CD, EF are concurrent.

7. **Pascal's theorem.**
   $ABCDEF$ is a hexagon inscribed in a circle. AB, DE meet at P; BC, EF meet at Q; CD, FA meet at R. Prove that P, Q, R are collinear. (The line is called the Pascal line.)
   (It should be noted that there are 60 possible hexagons that can be drawn given 6 points on the circumference of a circle, so there are 60 possible Pascal lines).

The Symmedian Point

Theorem 3
Let P, Q, R be defined on BC, CA, AB respectively such that $BP/PC = c^2/b^2, CQ/QA = a^2/c^2, AR/RB = b^2/a^2$, then

(i) AP, BQ, CR are concurrent at a point S called the symmedian point of triangle ABC.

(ii) Angles LAP, MBQ, NCR are bisected by the internal bisectors AU, BV, CW of angles A, B, C respectively.

(iii) If the tangents to the circumcircle ABC at B and C meet at A_0 and B_0, C_0 are similarly defined, then AA_0, BB_0, CC_0 are concurrent at S.

(iv) If the tangent to the circumcircle ABC at A meets BC at P_0 and Q_0, R_0 are similarly defined then P_0, Q_0, R_0 are collinear.

An outline proof is given.

(i) This is an immediate consequence of the converse of Ceva's theorem, and the areal co-ordinates of S are consequently $(a^2, b^2, c^2)/(a^2 + b^2 + c^2)$.

(ii) It is sufficient to show AU bisects $\angle LAP$. This can be done by proving $AP/AL = UP/UL$. Now $BU = ca/(b + c)$ and $BP = c^2 a/(b^2 + c^2)$, and so $UP = abc(b - c)/(b + c)(b^2 + c^2)$. Also $UL = ba/(b+c) - \frac{1}{2}a = a(b-c)/2(b+c)$. Thus $UP/UL = 2bc/(b^2 + c^2)$.
Next from Apollonius' theorem $AL^2 = \frac{1}{4}(2b^2 + 2c^2 - a^2)$. Now from the cosine rule for triangles ABP and ACP for c^2 and b^2 respectively, after eliminating $\cos(\angle APB)$ one finds $AP^2 = b^2 c^2 (2b^2 + 2c^2 - a^2)/(b^2 + c^2)^2$. Hence the result.

(iii) The concurrency of AA_0, BB_0, CC_0 is immediate from Ceva's theorem since $A_0 B = A_0 C$ etc. Let the point of concurrence be denoted by S_0. It remains to identify S_0 with S by proving that if $AS_0 A_0$ meets BC at P' then $BP' : P'C = c^2 : b^2$. This may be done using areas. Note that $\angle CBA_0 = \angle A$ (alternate segment theorem). Hence $\angle ABA_0 = 180^\circ - \angle BCA$ and so $[ABA_0] = \frac{1}{2}(AB)(A_0 B) \sin C = c^2 (A_0 B)/4R$. Similarly $[ACA_0] = b^2 (A_0 C)/4R$. The result follows since $A_0 B = A_0 C$.

(iv) This is an immediate consequence of Desargues's theorem since triangles ABC and $A_0 B_0 C_0$ are in perspective.

Exercises

8. Using the notation of Theorem 3 prove that QR passes through P_0, RP passes through Q_0 and PQ passes through R_0.

9. Using the notation of Theorem 3 prove that

$$(AP_0)(BQ_0)(CR_0) = (AQ_0)(BR_0)(CP_0) = (AR_0)(BP_0)(CQ_0).$$

10. Straight lines AP, BQ, CR are drawn through a general point K inside triangle ABC to meet BC, CA, AB respectively in P, Q, R. Prove that the straight lines drawn from A, B, C to bisect QR, RP, PQ respectively are concurrent. Prove also that the straight lines drawn from A, B, C parallel to QR, RP, PQ will meet the respectively opposite sides in three points that are collinear.

11. ABC is a triangle. AB is produced its own length to C', with A' and B' similarly defined. Prove that $UV = CC', VW = AA', WU = BB'$.

12. Let ABC be any triangle and P any point in its interior. Let P_1, P_2 be the feet of the perpendiculars from P to AC, BC respectively; Let Q_1, Q_2 be the feet of the perpendiculars from C to AP, BP respectively. Prove that, if P_1 and Q_2 do not coincide and P_2 and Q_1 do not coincide, then Q_1P_2, Q_2P_1 and AB are concurrent.

5.6   Unit 10: Hints and Solutions

1. $BX_0/X_0C = -c/b$ etc. The product of the three expressions is -1. Now use Menelaus's theorem.

2. Let the external bisector of $\angle BKC$ meet BC at U. Then $BU/UC = -BK/CK$ etc. The product of this with two similar expressions for CV/VA and AW/WB is equal to -1. Menelaus's theorem now produces the required result.

3. II_1 is perpendicular to I_2AI_3, so it is sufficient to prove P and Q lie on I_2AI_3, the equation of which is $cy + bz = 0$. Use Menelaus's theorem to show that the co-ordinates of W and V may be written as $(l, 0, c)/(l + c)$ and $(-l, b, 0)/(b - l)$ respectively, where l is a parameter designating the orientation of UVW. Now IV has equation $bcx + lcy = b(a + l)z$ and that of I_1W is $bcx + c(a+l)y = lbz$. Eliminating bcx one sees at once these meet on $cy + bz = 0$. Similarly the intersection of IW and I_1V lies on this line also.

4. Using standard notation the parallel sides mean that there exist constants l, m, n such that $\mathbf{u} - \mathbf{v} = l(\mathbf{x} - \mathbf{y}), \mathbf{v} - \mathbf{w} = m(\mathbf{y} - \mathbf{z}), \mathbf{w} - \mathbf{u} = n(\mathbf{z} - \mathbf{x})$. Add these equations and one gets $l = m = n$. If the common value is 1 then XU, YV, ZW are parallel, if not they are concurrent.

5. Let ABC, UVW be two distinct triangles and suppose P, Q, R defined by $P = BC \wedge VW, Q = CA \wedge WU, R = AB \wedge UV$ are collinear, then AU, BV, CW are either parallel or concurrent. Either the three lines are parallel or two of them, say AU and BV meet at K. Now let KC meet VW at W_0. Now apply Desargues's theorem to triangles ABC and UVW_0. Let UW_0 meet AC at Q_0, then by Desargues's theorem P, Q_0, R are collinear. But this cannot be true since Q is the only

point on AC which is collinear with P and R. Contradiction establishes the result.

6. Use Menelaus's theorem to show that CE and DF meet the line of centres UV of S_3 and S_4 at the same point, W. Since AC and BD both pass through U, AE and BF both pass through V and CE and DF both pass through W, the converse of Desargues's theorem implies triangle CAE and DBF are in perspective.

7. The proof of Pascal's theorem is very similar to that of Desargues's theorem. Extend AB, CD, EF to form a triangle XYZ. Write down the results obtained from Menelaus's theorem by considering BC, DE and FA as transversals of triangle XYZ. Multiply or divide these relations suitably to prove that PQR is a transversal of triangle XYZ, using the converse of Menelaus's theorem.

8. Use areas to show that $BP_0/P_0C = -c^2/b^2$ and the converse of Menelaus's theorem to show QRP_0 is a transversal of triangle ABC.

9. $P_0Q_0R_0$ is a transversal of triangle ABC. Also $(AP_0)^2 = (BP_0)(CP_0)$ etc., by the intersecting chord and tangent theorem.

10. Let K be the point (l, m, n), then P has co-ordinates $(0, m, n)/(m + n)$ and similarly for Q and R. The midpoint P_0 of QR has co-ordinates $(2l^2 + lm + nl, m(n + l), n(l + m))$ divided by $2(l+m)(n+l)$. The equation of AP_0 is $yn(l+m) = zm(n + l)$, and this means it cuts BC at a point with co-ordinates proportional to $(0, m(n + l), n(l + m))$. By symmetry AP_0, BQ_0 and CR_0 are concurrent at a point with co-ordinates proportional to

$(l(m + n), m(n + l), n(l + m))$. For the second part the line through A parallel to QR meets BC at a point P_1 with coordinates

$$(0, -m(n + l), n(l + m))/l(n - m),$$

so we must assume that no two of l, m, n are equal for the problem to be valid. Assuming this to be so we observe that P_1 divides BC externally in the ratio $n(l + m) : m(n + l)$, with similar ratios involving Q_1 and R_1. It now follows by Menelaus's theorem that P_1, Q_1, R_1 are collinear.

11. Apply Menelaus's theorem to triangle ABA' with transversal $C'CV$ and to triangle ACA' with transversal $B'BW$.

12. Establish that P_1, P_2, Q_1, Q_2, P and C lie on a circle and use Pascal's theorem on the hexagon $PQ_2P_1CP_2Q_1$.

Chapter 6

Geometrical Inequalities

6.1   Unit 12: Geometrical Inequalities: different versions of the same inequality

Geometrical, trigonometrical and algebraic presentations

Consider the following three exercises:

(1) If the radii of the circumcircle and the incircle are denoted by R and r respectively, prove that $R \geq 2r$.

(2) Let $A + B + C = 180^o$. Prove that $\sin \frac{1}{2}A \sin \frac{1}{2}B \sin \frac{1}{2}C \leq \frac{1}{8}$.

(3) If a, b, c are the sides of a non-degenerate triangle prove that

$$abc \geq (b + c - a)(c + a - b)(a + b - c).$$

Exercise 1 is a problem presented in geometrical form, Exercise 2 is one presented in trigonometrical form and Exercise 3 is one presented in algebraic form. It is sometimes easier when solving a problem to use known formulae to translate the problem from one form to another.

In order to illustrate these ideas we solve each of the exercises given above in the form stated and then show that they are in fact essentially one and the same problem, though they look very different at first sight. As far as Exercise 1 is concerned the method would be to go through the derivation of the formula $OI^2 = R^2 - 2Rr$ (see Chapter 4), and then to argue that the square of any length is non-negative, and hence $R \geq 2r$. Furthermore equality holds if and only if O and I coincide, which is known to be when the triangle is equilateral.

For Exercise 2 write $\frac{1}{2}A = x, \frac{1}{2}B = y, \frac{1}{2}C = z$, then

$$x + y + z = 90^o,$$

and $\sin x$, $\sin y$, $\sin z$, are positive, so by the Arithmetic Mean-Geometric Mean inequality one has

$$\sqrt[3]{(\sin x)(\sin y)(\sin z)} \leq \frac{1}{3}(\sin x + \sin y + \sin z)$$

with equality if and only if $x = y = z = 30^o$. Then one can argue that since the graph of $\sin t$ is concave (second derivative negative) then the point P representing $\sin 30^o = \frac{1}{2} = \sin\{(x+y+z)/3\}$ lies not below the centroid of the triangle XYZ representing

$$\frac{1}{3}(\sin x + \sin y + \sin z)$$

with coincidence if and only if X, Y, Z are one and the same point.

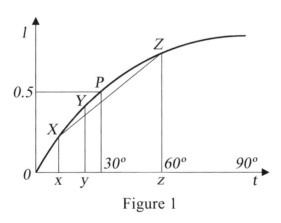

Figure 1

It follows that

$$\frac{1}{3}(\sin x + \sin y + \sin z) < \sin 30^o = \frac{1}{2},$$

and hence
$$\sin x \sin y \sin z \le \frac{1}{8}$$
with equality if and only if $x = y = z$, that is if and only if $A = B = C = 60°$.

Exercise 3 involves the side lengths a, b, c and all such problems are complicated by the existence of the constraints $b + c > a, c + a > b, a + b > c$. Almost always the best line of approach is to use the substitutions $a = m + n, b = n + l, c = l + m$, and then the constraints are converted into $l > 0, m > 0, n > 0$, constraints which are typically associated with the AM/GM inequality. Making the substitutions converts the required inequality into proving

$$(m + n)(n + l)(l + m) \ge 8lmn$$

for all positive l, m, n.
Now by the AG/GM inequality we have both $(l+m+n) \ge 3(lmn)^{\frac{1}{3}}$ and $(lm + mn + nl) \ge 3(lmn)^{\frac{2}{3}}$. Multiplying these together gives

$$(l + m + n)(lm + mn + nl) \ge 9lmn,$$

which on multiplying out and rearranging turns out to be equivalent to the required inequality. Equality occurs if and only if $l = m = n$, that is if and only if $a = b = c$.

As already mentioned the above three exercises are in fact one and the same problem. That (1) and (2) are equivalent follows from the formula $r = 4R \sin \frac{1}{2}A \sin \frac{1}{2}B \sin \frac{1}{2}C$. That (1) and (3) are equivalent follows after some algebra from the three formulae

$$R = \frac{abc}{4[ABC]}, \quad rs = [ABC] \text{ and } [ABC]^2 = s(s - a)(s - b)(s - c).$$

Sometimes, of course, problems are posed which involve a mixture of presentations, but the skills needed to solve a problem efficiently are (a) an ability to alter the presentation of the problem into the form in which it is most easily solved and (b) a knowledge of the basic algebraic methods used in treating inequalities, whether in a geometrical context or not.

Exercise

1. Find the trigonometrical and algebraic versions of the geometrical inequality $OH^2 \geq 0$.

We now give a review of the most common algebraic method needed when dealing with geometrical inequalities. This is the Arithmetic Mean/Geometric Mean (AM/GM) inequality.

2-dimensional form

If p, q are positive and the equation $x^2 - 2px + q^2 = 0$ has both roots u, v positive then $p \geq q$. This follows immediately by expressing the given equation in the form $(x - p)^2 = p^2 - q^2$. Since $u + v = 2p$ and $uv = q^2$, this means that

$$\frac{1}{2}(u + v) \geq \sqrt{uv},$$

and furthermore equality holds if and only if $p = q$, that is, if and only if $u = v$.

Exercises

2. In the above put u, v equal to $m, n; n, l; l, m$ successively in the AM/GM inequality and hence give an alternative proof

(to the one given in the text) of the inequality that for all positive l, m, n we have

$$(m+n)(n+l)(l+m) \geq 8lmn.$$

3. Let y_1, y_2, y_3, y_4 be four positive numbers. Put

$$u = \frac{1}{2}(y_1 + y_2), v = \frac{1}{2}(y_3 + y_4)$$

in $\frac{1}{2}(u + v) \geq \sqrt{uv}$ to deduce

$$\frac{1}{4}(y_1 + y_2 + y_3 + y_4) \geq (y_1 y_2 y_3 y_4)^{\frac{1}{4}},$$

with equality if and only if $y_1 = y_2 = y_3 = y_4$.

4. Let h be the harmonic mean of u, v defined by $1/u + 1/v = 2/h$. Prove that $h \leq \sqrt{uv}$ with equality if and only if $u = v$.

5. Put $y_4 = \frac{1}{3}(y_1 + y_2 + y_3)$ in Exercise 3 and deduce that if y_1, y_2, y_3 are three positive numbers then

$$\frac{1}{3}(y_1 + y_2 + y_3) \geq (y_1 y_2 y_3)^{\frac{1}{3}}.$$

6. Put $y_1 = s - a, y_2 = s - b, y_3 = s - c$ in Exercise 5 and use Heron's formula for $[ABC]$ to prove that a triangle with fixed perimeter has maximum area when it is equilateral.

3-dimensional form

If p, q, r are positive and if the equation $y^3 - 3py^2 + 3q^2y - r^3 = 0$ has three positive roots u, v, w then $p \geq q \geq r$. Since $u + v + w = 3p, uv + vw + wu = 3q^2, uvw = r^3$ this means

$$\frac{1}{3}(u + v + w) \geq \frac{1}{\sqrt{3}}(uv + vw + wu)^{\frac{1}{2}} \geq (uvw)^{\frac{1}{3}},$$

with equality if and only if $u = v = w$. The proof is as follows: $p \geq r$ has already been established in Exercise 5, but this is not enough as what we really need to show is that q lies between p and r. Replacing u, v, w by $U = vw, V = wu, W = uv$, by Exercise 5 we have $\frac{1}{3}(U + V + W) \geq (UVW)^{\frac{1}{3}}$. Taking positive square roots this gives $q \geq r$. Equality holds if and only if $uv = vw = wu$, that is if and only if $u = v = w$.

Finally $(u - v)^2 + (v - w)^2 + (w - u)^2 \geq 0$ with equality if and only if $u = v = w$. This implies that

$$(u + v + w)^2 \geq 3(uv + vw + wu),$$

which on taking positive square roots gives $p \geq q$.

Exercises

7. Let r be the radius of the incircle of a triangle of semi-perimeter s. Prove that $s \geq 3\sqrt{3}r$, with equality if and only if the triangle is equilateral.

8. Let H be the orthocentre of triangle ABC. Prove that

$$\frac{BC}{AH} \times \frac{CA}{BH} \times \frac{AB}{CH} = \frac{BC}{AH} + \frac{CA}{BH} + \frac{AB}{CH}$$

$$\geq 3\sqrt{3}.$$

6.2 Unit 12: Hints and Solutions

1. The trigonometrical version is $\cos 2A + \cos 2B + \cos 2C \geq -\frac{3}{2}$, and the algebraic version is

   $$a^2(b^2+c^2-a^2)^2 + b^2(c^2+a^2-b^2)^2 + c^2(a^2+b^2-c^2)^2 \geq 3a^2b^2c^2.$$

   The best way to solve this is to choose O as the origin of vectors and to use $\mathbf{OH} = \mathbf{OA} + \mathbf{OB} + \mathbf{OC}$.

2. Multiply the three results together. It is in fact an easier proof than the one in the text.

3. Of course the two dimensional form of the AM/GM inequality has to be used three times, once with u, v then again with y_1, y_2 and finally with y_3, y_4. This provides the AG/GM inequality in 4 dimensions. The same trick can be used to establish the inequality in 8, 16, ... dimensions.

4. Show $h = 2uv/(u+v)$ and then use $(u+v)/2 \geq \sqrt{uv}$.

5. This is entirely straightforward and provides the AM/GM inequality in 3 dimensions. The same trick can be employed to establish the inequality in $7, 6, \ldots, 15, 14, \ldots$ etc. dimensions.

6. $[ABC]^2 = sy_1y_2y_3 \leq \frac{s}{3}(y_1+y_2+y_3) = \frac{s^2}{3}$ with equality if and only if $a = b = c$.

7. You will need to use $\frac{1}{3}(a+b+c) \geq (abc)^{\frac{1}{3}}$, $abc/4R = [ABC] = rs$ and $R \geq 2r$.

8. The first part follows from the fact that if $A + B + C = 180^o$ then $\tan A + \tan B + \tan C = \tan A \tan B \tan C$. The inequality comes from using this together with the three dimensional form of the AM/GM inequality with $u = \tan A, v = \tan B, w = \tan C$.

6.3   Unit 13: Geometrical Inequalities: other algebraic methods

Jensen's Theorem

If $f(x)$ is a convex function on the interval $a < x < b$ (i.e. with a graph curved like $y = x^2$), then with $a < x_1 < x_2 < b$ we have

$$f\left(\frac{x_1 + x_2}{2}\right) < \frac{f(x_1) + f(x_2)}{2}.$$

In Figure 1 this theorem is illustrated and arises from the fact that $AP < AQ$, where A is the ordinate corresponding to $\frac{1}{2}(x_1 + x_2)$.

Note that $d^2 f/dx^2 > 0$ is a sufficient condition for f to be a convex function.

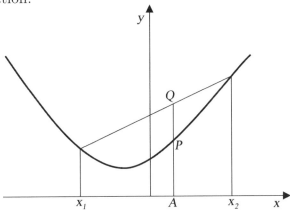

Figure 1

Likewise if $a < x_1 < x_2 < x_3 < b$ and f is convex, then

$$f\left(\frac{1}{3}(x_1 + x_2 + x_3)\right) < \frac{1}{3}\{f(x_1) + f(x_2) + f(x_3)\}.$$

For concave functions the direction of these inequalities are reversed; consider $y - \sin x$ on the interval $0° < x < 180°$ for example.

An example involving three points using the function $\sin x$ was given in Unit 12, so the general case need not be explained further, as the reasoning is exactly the same as in that case.

Positive Definite Quadratic Forms

Theorem 1

Let a, b, c be real constants and x, y real variables that are not both zero then the function $f(x, y) = ax^2 + 2bxy + cy^2 > 0$ if and only if $a > 0$ and $ac > b^2$.

The proof is immediate by the process of **completing the square** (a skill that is a great asset and one that is rarely taught effectively at school level any more). What it amounts to here is to express

$$f(x, y) = \frac{(ax + by)^2 + (ac - b^2)y^2}{a}.$$

Theorem 1 generalizes to functions of several variables. For example with the three variables x, y, z not all zero simultaneously the function $f(x, y, z)$ given by

$$f(x, y, z) = ax^2 + by^2 + cz^2 + 2fyz + 2gzx + 2hxy > 0$$

if and only if $a > 0, ab - h^2 > 0$ and the 3×3 determinant

$$\det \begin{pmatrix} a & h & g \\ h & b & f \\ g & f & c \end{pmatrix} > 0.$$

Exercise

1. If x, y, z are real variables, not all of which vanish simultaneously, and A, B, C are the angles of a triangle, prove that

$$x^2 + y^2 + z^2 - (2yz \cos A + 2zx \cos B + 2xy \cos C) \geq 0$$

and find with proof when equality occurs.

The Cauchy-Schwarz Inequality

Let $\mathbf{x} = (x_1, x_2, x_3)$, $\mathbf{y} = (y_1, y_2, y_3)$ then $\mathbf{x}.\mathbf{y} = |\mathbf{x}||\mathbf{y}| \cos \theta$, where θ is the angle between the directions of $\mathbf{x}$ and $\mathbf{y}$. Since $\cos^2 \theta \leq 1$ it follows that

$$(\mathbf{x}.\mathbf{y})^2 \leq |\mathbf{x}|^2 |\mathbf{y}|^2$$

or $$(x_1 y_1 + x_2 y_2 + x_3 y_3)^2 \leq (x_1^2 + x_2^2 + x_3^2)(y_1^2 + y_2^2 + y_3^2).$$

Exercise

2. Let P be a point in the interior of triangle ABC, and let d, e, f denote the distances from P to the sides of the triangle. Let a, b, c denote the lengths of these sides respectively. Show that the minimum value of $a/d + b/e + c/f$ occurs when P is at the incentre of triangle ABC.

The Power Means Inequality

If x_1, x_2, x_3 are real and positive, then

$$\{(x_1 + x_2 + x_3)/3\}^s \quad \begin{array}{l} \leq \frac{1}{3}(x_1^s + x_2^s + x_3^s), \quad \text{if} \quad s < 0 \quad \text{or} \quad s > 1, \\ \geq \frac{1}{3}(x_1^s + x_2^s + x_3^s), \quad \quad \text{if} \quad 0 < s < 1. \end{array}$$

or

This is a special case of Jonsen's theorem for $f(x) = x^s$.

Trigonometrical methods

Sometimes trigonometrical inequalities are most easily solved by transforming them into the equivalent algebraic form by means of the sine and cosine formulae, otherwise considerable skill may be required that can be obtained only by familiarity and practice with basic trigonometrical formulae, including the sum and product rules and those involving double and half angles. Quite often the AM/GM inequality or Jensen's theorem is needed as a final step.

Exercises

3. Suppose that A, B, C are the angles of a triangle. Prove that

$$\sin^2 A + \sin^2 B + \sin^2 C < 2(\sin B \sin C + \sin C \sin A + \sin A \sin B).$$

4. Let a, b, c be the sides of triangle ABC and let I be the incentre. Prove that

$$(bc + ca + ab) \geq (AI + BI + CI)^2.$$

5. If A, B, C are the angles of a triangle, then prove that

$$(1 - \cos A)(1 - \cos B)(1 - \cos C) \geq \cos A \cos B \cos C.$$

A number of additional exercises are now given to illustrate the various techniques described above.

Exercises

6. If a, b, c are the sides of a triangle, then prove

(i) $3a^2 + 6b^2 > 2c^2$;

(ii) $2(b^2c^2 + c^2a^2 + a^2b^2) - (a^4 + b^4 + c^4) > 0.$

7. G is the centroid of the acute-angled triangle ABC and R is the circumradius. Show that

$$3R^2 \geq AG^2 + BG^2 + CG^2 > 8R^2/3.$$

8. Let a, b, c be the sides of a triangle and let l, d denote the lengths of the median, altitude respectively through A. Prove that

$$\frac{l}{d} \geq \frac{b^2 + c^2}{2bc}.$$

9. Given a triangle ABC, let I be the centre of the inscribed circle. The internal bisectors of the angles A, B, C meet the opposite sides in U, V, W respectively. Prove that

$$\frac{1}{4} < \frac{(AI)(BI)(CI)}{(AU)(BU)(CU)} \leq \frac{8}{27}.$$

10. The sides of a triangle are denoted as usual by a, b, c. Prove that

$$\{(a+b)^2 - c^2\}\{(b+c)^2 - a^2\}\{(c+a)^2 - b^2\} \leq 27a^2b^2c^2.$$

11. In a convex quadrilateral $ABCD$ let E be the intersection of AC and BD. Prove that

$$[ABE]^{\frac{1}{2}} + [CDE]^{\frac{1}{2}} \leq \{\text{Area}(ABCD)\}^{\frac{1}{2}}.$$

12. With the usual notation prove that

$$bc(s-a)^2 + ca(s-b)^2 + ab(s-c)^2 \geq \frac{1}{2}(sabc).$$

13. With the usual notation prove that

$$s \geq a \cos A + b \cos B + c \cos C.$$

14. Given a line l and two distinct points A and B on the same side of l, locate the points P on l so that the following expressions have maximum or minimum values:

  (i) $AP + BP$;

  (ii) $\angle APB$;

  (iii) $AP^2 + BP^2$;

  (iv) AP/BP.

15. Let a, b, c be the sides of triangle ABC. Let l, m, n be the lengths of the medians. Extend each median to the circumcircle and let the lengths of these extended chords be l', m', n' respectively. Prove that

$$l' + m' + n' \geq \frac{4}{3}(l + m + n)$$

and

$$l' + m' + n' \geq \frac{2}{\sqrt{3}}(a + b + c).$$

6.4   Unit 13: Hints and Solutions

1. This is an exercise in completing the square. The function on the left hand side becomes

   $$(x - z\cos B - y\cos C)^2 + (z\sin B - y\sin C)^2.$$

   You need to use $\cos A = -\cos(B+C)$ in deriving this. Note that as the function is expressible as the sum of two rather than three squares it is positive semi-definite, rather than positive definite. The implication of this in this exercise is that there is a line in 3-space for which equality holds, and this is easily seen to be $x = k\sin A, y = k\sin B, z = k\sin C$, where k is any real constant. This is where both brackets vanish simultaneously.

2.
   $$(a + b + c)^2 \leq (ad + be + cf)(a/d + b/e + c/f)$$

   by the Cauchy-Schwarz inequality. But $ad + be + cf = 2[ABC]$. Hence $a/d + b/e + c/f \geq 2s^2/[ABC]$. Equality occurs and the minimum is achieved when $(ad)^{\frac{1}{2}}/(a/d)^{\frac{1}{2}} = (be)^{\frac{1}{2}}/(b/e)^{\frac{1}{2}} = (cf)^{\frac{1}{2}}/(c/f)^{\frac{1}{2}}$, that is when $d = e = f$. So the minimum value is attained when P is the incentre.

3. The sine formula shows it is sufficient to prove that

   $$a^2 + b^2 + c^2 - 2(bc + ca + ab) < 0.$$

   Now put $a = m + n, b = n + l, c = l + m$, where l, m, n are positive (as suggested in Unit 12) and the left hand side becomes $-4(mn + nl + lm)$.

4. Use $AI = r\,\mathrm{cosec}\,\frac{1}{2}A$ etc. and $a = r(\cot\frac{1}{2}B + \cot\frac{1}{2}C)$ etc. You will need to use

   $$\sin(\frac{1}{2}A + \frac{1}{2}B + \frac{1}{2}C) = 1$$

and

$$\sin(x+y+z) = \sin x \cos y \cos z + \cos x \sin y \cos z \\ + \cos x \cos y \sin z - \sin x \sin y \sin z.$$

After cancelling common factors the inequality is reduced to proving $\sin \frac{1}{2}A+\sin \frac{1}{2}B+\sin \frac{1}{2}C \le \frac{3}{2}$ and for this use Jensen's theorem.

5. Use the cosine formula to transform the inequality into

$$(b+c-a)^2(c+a-b)^2(a+b-c)^2$$
$$\ge (b^2+c^2-a^2)(c^2+a^2-b^2)(a^2+b^2-c^2).$$

Then show that

$$(a-b+c)^2(a+b-c)^2 \ge (a^2-b^2+c^2)(a^2+b^2-c^2)$$

with equality if and only if $b=c$ or $A=90^\circ$. Then multiply this with two similar inequalities provided by cyclic change of letters.

6. In the first part use $a+b>c$, and the inequality holds even when $a=2b$. In the second part use $[ABC]>0$ and Heron's formula.

7. From Apollonius's theorem

$$AG^2 + BG^2 + CG^2 = (a^2+b^2+c^2)/3,$$

so the left hand inequality reduces to

$$\sin^2 A + \sin^2 B + \sin^2 C \le \frac{9}{4}$$

and the right hand inequality to showing that the same expression is strictly greater than 2. Beware in the last part of saying that it is obviously equal when the triangle degenerates; there is a perfectly good argument which begins by putting $1 - \sin^2 B = \cos^2 B, 1 - \sin^2 C = \cos^2 C$ and $\sin A = \sin(B + C) = \sin B \cos C + \sin C \cos B$. You also need to use the fact that the triangle is acute, so that B and C are acute, but $B + C$ is obtuse, leading to $\tan B \tan C > 1$ (as $\tan(B + C)$ is negative). For the first part see Unit 12 Exercise 1.

8. Express l^2 and d^2 in terms of a, b, c and then show that $16b^2c^2l^2 - 4d^2(b^2+c^2)^2$ comes to an expression that is a perfect square.

9. $AI/AU = (b+c)/(a+b+c)$. In fact the inequalities hold when I is replaced by any other point P internal to the triangle. For if P has areal co-ordinates (l, m, n), then

$$AP/AU = (m + n)/(l + m + n)$$

and the same reasoning holds.

10. Convert into a trigonometrical exercise using formulae for the area of a triangle. The inequality transforms to $\sin A + \sin B + \sin C \leq 3\sqrt{3}/2$ for which Jensen's theorem may be used.

11. Write the areas in terms of the lengths of the line segments EA, EB, EC, ED and $\angle AEB$. Use the AM/GM inequality on $(EA)(ED)$ and $(EB)(EC)$ after squaring.

12. Let x, y, z be any three positive real numbers. Clearly

$$(x^2 - y^2)(x - y) > 0,$$

whether $x \geq y$ or $x \leq y$. Sum three such inequalities and rearrange them to obtain

$$x^3 + y^3 + z^3 + xyz \geq \frac{1}{2}(y + z)(z + x)(x + y).$$

Finally set $x = b + c - a, y = c + a - b, z = a + b - c$ and the result follows.

13. Prove that $a \geq b \cos B + c \cos C$ by using the sine rule to convert it into a simple trigonometrical inequality. Then add two similar inequalities for the result.

14. Let A', B' be the feet of the perpendiculars from A, B on l. (i) Minimum when $\angle APA' = \angle BPB'$; (ii) Maximum when circle ABP touches l at P; (iii) Minimum when P is the midpoint of $A'B'$; (iv) Minimum if $AA' < BB'$ when k is such that the Apollonius circle $AP/BP = k$ touches l at P.

15. First prove that $3(a^2 + b^2 + c^2) \geq (a + b + c)^2$ and similarly for l, m, n in place of a, b, c. Use these two inequalities together with Apollonius's theorem to show $4k \geq \frac{4}{3}(l + m + n)$ and $4k \geq (2/\sqrt{3})(a + b + c)$, where $4k^2 = a^2 + b^2 + c^2$. Now use the intersecting chords theorem to show that $ll' = \frac{2}{3}(k^2 + l^2)$ and hence that $l' \geq 4k/3$. Hence $l' + m' + n' \geq 4k$.

6.5 Unit 14: Squares of distances, geodesics and the Fermat point

Introduction

Geometrical inequalities seem to fall into two classes. These are exemplified by Exercises 12 and 14 from Unit 13. Exercise 12 is really an algebraic inequality and though the lengths a, b, c, s are used it is not possible to see what the result means geometrically. Exercise 14 on the other hand, presents geometrical situations and the solutions to the four parts are interesting and one feels that by appreciating the results to the various parts one has gained some insight and learned some geometry.

In Unit 14 it is on the second class that we now concentrate, and each of the three sections contains a powerful result; and the last part on the Fermat (or Steiner) point is a justly famous result (with obvious generalizations to figures other than triangles).

Squares of distances

Theorem 1

Let ABC be a triangle and K a point with areal co-ordinates (l, m, n). Now suppose P is any other point in the plane of the triangle. Then

$$lAP^2 + mBP^2 + nCP^2 = lAK^2 + mBK^2 + nCK^2 + PK^2.$$

Proof

Take any suitable origin and write $\mathbf{OP} = \mathbf{p}, \mathbf{OA} = \mathbf{a}$, with similar small letters for other position vectors $\mathbf{OB}, \mathbf{OC}, \mathbf{OK}$. Then the left hand side is equal to

$$l(\mathbf{p} - \mathbf{a}).(\mathbf{p} - \mathbf{a}) + m(\mathbf{p} - \mathbf{b}).(\mathbf{p} - \mathbf{b}) + n(\mathbf{p} - \mathbf{c}).(\mathbf{p} - \mathbf{c})$$
$$= lOA^2 + mOB^2 + nOC^2 + OP^2 - 2\mathbf{p}.(l\mathbf{a} + m\mathbf{b} + n\mathbf{c})$$
$$= lOA^2 + mOB^2 + nOC^2 + OP^2 - 2\mathbf{OP}.\mathbf{OK}.$$

Note the use of $l + m + n = 1$.

By letting P coincide with K in this expression, the right hand side of the desired equality is seen to be

$$lOA^2 + mOB^2 + nOC^2 + OK^2 - 2OK^2 + PK^2.$$

That the two sides of the desired equality are actually equal now follows from the fact that $PK^2 = OP^2 - 2\mathbf{OP}.\mathbf{OK} + OK^2$.

Corollary

$$lAP^2 + mBP^2 + nCP^2 \geq lAK^2 + mBK^2 + nCK^2$$

with equality if and only if P coincides with K.

This result is immediate from Theorem 1 since $PK^2 \geq 0$.   ■

Exercises

1. ABC is a given triangle. Find the position of the point P such that $AP^2 + BP^2 + CP^2$ has its least value.

2. ABC is a given triangle. Find the position of the point P such that

$$(BC)(AP)^2 + (CA)(BP)^2 + (AB)(CP)^2$$

has its least value.

3. ABC is a given triangle. Find the position for P for which the expression

$$\tan A(AP)^2 + \tan B(BP)^2 + \tan C(CP)^2$$

has its least value.

4. Generalize Theorem 1 to involve n points in a plane.

5. ABC is a given triangle with orthocentre H. Find the position of the point P such that $(AP^2 + BP^2 + CP^2 + HP^2)$ has its least value.

6. If H and T are respectively the orthocentre and nine-point centre of triangle ABC prove that

$$AT^2 + BT^2 + CT^2 \leq 3R^2 \leq AH^2 + BH^2 + CH^2.$$

7. Let ABC be a triangle, area $[ABC]$. Show that the interior of the circumcircle and its boundary is the set union of all points P satisfying the inequality

$$2[ABC] \leq \sin 2A(AP)^2 + \sin 2B(BP)^2 + \sin 2C(CP)^2 \leq 4[ABC].$$

8. Prove that if P lies on the incircle of triangle ABC then

$$a(AP)^2 + b(BP)^2 + c(CP)^2 = 2[ABC](r + 2R).$$

9. Let $P_1P_2P_3 \ldots P_n$ be an n sided polygon inscribed in a circle of unit radius. Prove that

$$\sum_{k=2}^{n} \sum_{l=1}^{k-1} (P_k P_l)^2 \leq n^2.$$

Geodesics

Strictly speaking a geodesic is the shortest path from one point
to another subject to certain constraints such as passing through
a third point or meeting a given line. For example for two non-
antipodal points on the surface of a sphere, with the path con-
strained to lie of the surface, the geodesic is the shorter arc of the
great circle passing through the two points. For a pair of antipodal
points, all great semicircles joining the points are geodesics. More
generally we may extend the definition of a geodesic problem to
include one involving the minimization of sums of distances. If one
allows this extension then the problem of the Fermat point is a
geodesic problem, though it is such a celebrated problem that we
postpone discussion of it to the third and final section of the Unit.

The simplest geodesic problem with a constraint is widely known
and has already been set as the first part of Exercise 14 of Unit 13,
but the full solution is worth looking at. A and B are two points
on the same side of a line l, and one has to find the shortest distance from A to B, with the constraint that the path must touch
l. What one does is to reflect the point A in l to produce the
point A_0. Then join A_0B to intersect l at P. P is the point that
minimizes $(AP + PB)$. It is the shortest path because $AP = A_0P$
and A_0B is minimized in length when it is in a straight line. The
reason this problem is widely known is that it is analogous to the
optical problem of a light ray being reflected from a mirror. Light
rays travel along paths of least time.

Exercises

10. Two lines l and m are given, perpendicular to one another,
    and A and B are two distinct points lying in the same quad-
    rant formed by the two lines. Suppose that A is nearer to

l than B and that B is nearer to m than A. Show how to locate points P, Q lying on l, m respectively such that $(AP + PQ + QB)$ is minimized and the path $APQB$ lies in the same quadrant as A and B. Is the path unique?

11. ABC is an equilateral triangle of side 6. P is fixed and lies on AB such that $AP = 4$ and $PB = 2$. Q and R lie on BC and CA respectively, so that Q lies between B and C, and R lies between C and A.

(i) Show how to choose Q and R to minimize $(PQ + QR)$ and calculate its minimum value.

(ii) Show how to choose Q and R to minimize $(PQ + QR + RP)$ and calculate its minimum value.

The final and most complicated problem of the type illustrated by such exercises is as follows. If ABC is an acute-angled triangle and P, Q, R are internal points of BC, CA, AB respectively, how do we choose them so that $(PQ + QR + RP)$ is minimized? The answer arises from the known fact that if D, E, F are the feet of the perpendiculars from the vertices on to the opposite sides, then AD, BE, CF bisect the angles of the pedal triangle DEF. In other words P, Q, R should be chosen to coincide with D, E, F respectively. To actually illustrate diagrammatically that this is a geodesic requires five reflections and six copies of the triangle.

The Fermat Point

If ABC is a triangle all of whose angles are less than $120°$, then a point P exists internal to the triangle such that $\angle BPC = \angle CPA = \angle APB = 120°$. In order to construct the point P draw equilateral triangles $A'BC, AB'C, ABC'$ so that A' is on the opposite side of BC to A and similarly for B' and C'. See Figure 1

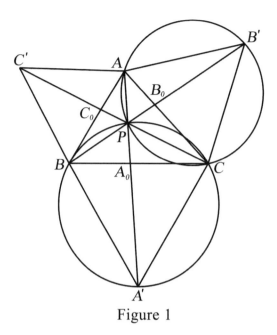

Figure 1

Theorem 1

The circumcircles of triangles $A'BC, AB'C, ABC'$ meet at a point P such that

$$\angle BPC = \angle CPA = \angle APB = 120^o,$$

and furthermore APA', BPB', CPC' are straight lines with $AA' = BB' = CC'$.

Proof

Let the circumcircles $A'BC, AB'C$ meet P as well as C. Then, by the cyclic quadrilateral property $\angle BPC = \angle CPA = 120^o$. It follows that $\angle APB = 120^o$ also. Since $\angle BC'A = 60^o$ we have $APBC'$ is a cyclic quadrilateral and hence the three circumcircles meet at P. Now since this is so, $\angle C'PB = \angle C'AB$ (angles in the same segment)$= 60^o$. But $\angle BPC = 120^o$, and hence $C'PC$ is a straight line. Similarly $A'PA$ and $B'PB$ are straight line.

Now from Ptolemy's theorem for the cyclic quadrilateral $PCA'B$, since triangle $CA'B$ is equilateral, we have $PA' = PB + PC$, hence $AA' = PA + PB + PC$. Similarly $BB' = CC' = PA + PB + PC = AA'$. ∎

Theorem 2

If Q is any point in the interior of triangle ABC distinct from P then

$$(QA + QB + QC) > (PA + PB + PC).$$

The extension to Ptolemy's theorem states that if $WXYZ$ is not a cyclic quadrilateral then $(WX)(YZ) + (XY)(ZW) > (WY)(XZ)$. Consider therefore the quadrilateral $QCA'B$. If Q does not lie on the arc BPC, then since triangle $CA'B$ is equilateral, it follows from the extension to Ptolemy's theorem that $QB + QC > QA'$. And hence that $QA + QB + QC > QA + QA' \geq AA'$. Thus

$$(QA + QB + QC) > (PA + PB + PC).$$

Similarly this inequality is also true unless Q lies additionally on the arcs CPA and APB. It therefore holds for all internal points of triangle ABC distinct from P.

Theorems 1 and 2 establish the property of the Fermat point P for triangles ABC all of whose angles are less than $120°$.

Exercises

12. Where is the Fermat point located in a triangle ABC for which angle $BAC > 120°$?

13. Let $AP = l, BP = m, CP = n$, where P is the Fermat point of triangle ABC (with all its angles less that $120°$). Suppose

AP meets BC at A_0 with B_0 and C_0 similarly defined (see Figure 1). Establish the following results:

(i) $BA_0/A_0C = m/n$;

(ii) The areal co-ordinates of P are

$$(mn, nl, lm)/(mn + nl + lm).$$

(iii) $1/A_0P = 1/BP + 1/CP$.

14. Prove that

$$2(AP + BP + CP)^2 = a^2 + b^2 + c^2 + 4\sqrt{3}[ABC],$$

where P is the Fermat point of triangle ABC (with all its angles less than 120°) and $[ABC]$ is the area.

6.6 Unit 14: Hints and Solutions

1. Take $l = m = n = \frac{1}{3}$. The answer, from Theorem 1, is G.

2. Take $l = a/(a+b+c)$, $m = b/(a+b+c)$, $n = c/(a+b+c)$. The answer, from Theorem 1, is I. What happens if the sign of c is changed?

3. H, since the co-ordinates of H are proportional to the tangents.

4. Replace A, B, C by $A_1, A_2, \ldots, A_n$ and l, m, n by $l_1, l_2, \ldots, l_n$ and $l + m + n = 1$ by

$$l_1 + l_2 + \ldots + l_n = 1.$$

5. Use the result of Exercise 4 with each of the $l_k, k = 1$ to 4, being equal to $\frac{1}{4}$. Take the origin to be the circumcentre and use $\mathbf{OH} = \mathbf{OA} + \mathbf{OB} + \mathbf{OC}$. The answer is T, the nine-point centre, since $OT = \frac{1}{2}(\mathbf{OA} + \mathbf{OB} + \mathbf{OC})$.

6. From Theorem 1

$$AP^2 + BP^2 + CP^2 = AG^2 + BG^2 + CG^2 + 3PG^2.$$

Then put P successively equal to H and T. You will need $OH^2 = 9R^2 - (a^2 + b^2 + c^2) \geq 0$, and also $GH^2 = OH^2/9$ and $GT^2 = OH^2/36$.

7. Take P to be O, providing the lower bound $2[ABC]$. Then take P to be A or B or C, providing the upper bound $4[ABC]$. You will need the formula $4[ABC] = abc/R$.

8. Take P to be the point X (or Y or Z), where the incircle touches the side BC. You will need to calculate the length of AX.

9. Put $\mathbf{P}_k\mathbf{P}_l = \mathbf{OP}_l - \mathbf{OP}_k$. Equality holds if and only if

$$\mathbf{OP_1} + \mathbf{OP_2} + \ldots + \mathbf{OP_n} = \mathbf{0},$$

as, for example, with a regular polygon.

10. A double reflection. Yes, the answer is unique.

11.   (i) Let P_0 be the reflection of P in BC. Draw P_0R perpendicular to AC to meet BC in Q and CA in R. The minimum value of $(PQ + QR)$ is $3\sqrt{3}$.

  (ii) Let P_0 be the reflection of P in BC and P_1 the reflection of P in AC. $P_0P_1 = PQ + QR + RP$ is the minimum path and its length is $2\sqrt{21}$. In proving this note that $PQ : QR : RP = PB : RC : AR = BQ : QC : AP$ leading to $RP = 2l/5$ and $PQ = l/4$, where l is the required path length.

12. A. It seems obvious enough, but you need to **prove** that if Q is any point internal to triangle ABC, then

$$(QA + QB + QC) > (BA + CA).$$

13. For the first part note that PA_0 is the internal bisector of angle BPC and hence $BA_0/A_0C = BP/CP$. Part two follows immediately (see the notes on Ceva's theorem in Chapter 5). For the final part use $a^2 = m^2 + n^2 + mn$ and the formula for the length of the internal bisector of an angle to show that

$$(A_0P)^2 = mn(m + n - a)(m + n + a)/(m + n)^2.$$

The result follows immediately.

14. Using the notation of Exercise 13 we have $a^2 = m^2 + n^2 + mn$, $b^2 = n^2 + l^2 + nl$, $c^2 = l^2 + m^2 + lm$. Solve for l, m, n. Work with $t = l + m + n$ as an auxiliary variable. Heron's formula for $[ABC]$ is required.

Chapter 7

Vectors, Co-ordinate Geometry and Inversion

7.1 Unit 15: The circumcentre as origin

The Euler line again

In all areas of mathematics it is found that certain special techniques are useful in connection with certain types of problem. In this Unit we show how the use of vectors with the circumcentre as origin provides an alternative treatment to the pure geometrical methods introduced in Chapter 4, to problems associated with the Euler line of triangle ABC. (The use of areal co-ordinates for problems involving the circumcentre, the orthocentre and the nine-point centre is not normally advisable.)

If the circumcentre O is chosen as the origin of position vectors, then all vectors from O to points on the circumcircle have the same modulus R, the radius of the circumcircle. Thus if P and Q are two such points with position vectors $\mathbf{p}$ and $\mathbf{q}$ respectively, we have

$$(\mathbf{p} + \mathbf{q})(\mathbf{p} - \mathbf{q}) = p^2 - q^2 = R^2 - R^2 = 0,$$

and hence $(\mathbf{p}+\mathbf{q})$ is perpendicular to $(\mathbf{p}-\mathbf{q})$. If K is the midpoint of PQ this means that $\mathbf{OK}$ is perpendicular to $\mathbf{PQ}$. Note how easily in this framework is it shown that the perpendicular bisector of the chord of a circle passes through its centre. Indeed any line parallel to $\mathbf{OK}$ is perpendicular to $\mathbf{PQ}$.

Writing $\mathbf{a}, \mathbf{b}, \mathbf{c}$, for the position vectors of A, B, C respectively, we note that $a^2 = b^2 = c^2 = R^2$ and $\mathbf{b}.\mathbf{c} = R^2 \cos 2A$, $\mathbf{c}.\mathbf{a} = R^2 \cos 2B$ and $\mathbf{a}.\mathbf{b} = R^2 \cos 2C$. These equations specify the metric for working out distances and angles using co-ordinates in this system.

The midpoints L, M, N, of BC, CA, AB, have vector positions

$$\frac{1}{2}(\mathbf{b} + \mathbf{c}), \ \frac{1}{2}(\mathbf{c} + \mathbf{a}), \ \frac{1}{2}(\mathbf{a} + \mathbf{b})$$

respectively. From the argument in the second paragraph the displacement from the point A with vector position $\mathbf{a}$ to the point P with vector position $(\mathbf{a} + \mathbf{b} + \mathbf{c})$, being equal to $(\mathbf{b} + \mathbf{c})$, represents a line parallel to OL and perpendicular to BC. The point P therefore lies on the perpendicular to BC through A. Similarly it lies on the other two altitudes. Hence the point P coincides with the orthocentre H, the vector position of which is thus $(\mathbf{a} + \mathbf{b} + \mathbf{c})$. It follows that $\mathbf{OG} = \frac{1}{3}\mathbf{OH}$, where G is the centroid with vector position $\frac{1}{3}(\mathbf{a} + \mathbf{b} + \mathbf{c})$ and hence OGH is a straight line, the Euler line of triangle ABC. The point T defined by $\mathbf{OT} = \frac{1}{2}\mathbf{OH}$ also lies on this line. Furthermore G and H divide OT internally and externally respectively in the ratio 2:1.

Now $\mathbf{OH} = \mathbf{OA} + \mathbf{AH}$, so $\mathbf{AH} = (\mathbf{b} + \mathbf{c}) = 2\mathbf{OL}$. Similarly $\mathbf{BH} = 2\mathbf{OM}$ and $\mathbf{CH} = 2\mathbf{ON}$. It follows that if D_0, E_0, F_0 are the midpoints of AH, BH, CH, respectively, then $\mathbf{AD_0} = \mathbf{D_0H} = \mathbf{OL}, \mathbf{BE_0} = \mathbf{E_0H} = \mathbf{OM}$ and $\mathbf{CF} = \mathbf{F_0H} = \mathbf{ON}$.

The following set of exercises should be attempted using the same vector framework as above.

Exercises

1. Prove that T is the centre of a circle of radius $\frac{1}{2}R$ passing through the nine points $L, M, N, D, E, F, D_0, E_0, F_0$. (Here D_0 is the midpoint of AH, E_0 that of BH and F_0 that of CH.)

2. Prove that O is the orthocentre of triangle LMN.

3. Let X, Y, Z be defined by the vector equations

$$\mathbf{OX} = -\mathbf{a} + \mathbf{b} + \mathbf{c}, \mathbf{OY} = \mathbf{a} - \mathbf{b} + \mathbf{c}, \mathbf{OZ} = \mathbf{a} + \mathbf{b} - \mathbf{c}.$$

Establish the following facts about triangle XYZ in relation to triangle ABC.

(a) The circumcentre S of triangle XYZ is the orthocentre of triangle ABC.

(b) Triangles ABC, XYZ have a common centroid.

(c) The orthocentre K of triangle XYZ and the circumcentre O of triangle ABC both lie on HG extended and O is the midpoint of HK.

4. If U, V, W are the reflections of the circumcentre of triangle ABC in its sides BC, CA, AB respectively, prove that AU, BV, CW are concurrent. Locate the point of concurrence.

5. O is the centre of a circle $A_1 A_2 A_3$ of unit radius; another equal circle, centre P_1 is drawn through A_2, A_3. P_2 and P_3 are similarly defined. Prove that the points P_1, P_2, P_3 lie on a circle of unit radius. Let Q_4 be the centre of this circle. Now add a fourth point A_4 to the initial circle and repeat the above process with every set of three points from A_1, A_2, A_3, A_4 giving four circles, Q_1, Q_2, Q_3, Q_4. Prove that Q_1, Q_2, Q_3, Q_4 lie on a circle of unit radius, centre X. Find the vector position X in terms of those of A_1, A_2, A_3, A_4.

6. $ABCD$ is a cyclic quadrilateral. Consider the four triangles BCD, ACD, ABD, ABC. Show

(a) Their centroids form a quadrilateral similar to $ABCD$;

(b) The centres of their nine-point circles form a quadrilateral similar to $ABCD$;

(c) Their orthocentres form a quadrilateral congruent to $ABCD$.

7.2 Unit 15: Hints and Solutions

1. Prove that $\mathbf{TL} = -\frac{1}{2}\mathbf{a}$ and $\mathbf{TD_0} = \frac{1}{2}\mathbf{a}$ so that LD_0 is a diameter of the Nine-Point Circle of length R. Do not bother to work out the length of $\mathbf{TD}$ using vectors, for since $HOLD$ is a right-angled trapezium with T the midpoint of OH it is obvious that $TD = TL = \frac{1}{2}R$.

2. Prove that $\mathbf{TL} + \mathbf{TM} + \mathbf{TN} = \mathbf{TO}$ and explain why this is sufficient to establish the result.

3. (a) The point S with position vector $\mathbf{a} + \mathbf{b} + \mathbf{c}$ satisfies $\mathbf{XS} = 2\mathbf{a}$, so that the distance from S to X is $2R$. Similarly the distance from S to Y and the distance from S to Z is equal to $2R$ also.

   (b) One third the sum of the vector positions of the vertices is, for both triangles, equal to $\frac{1}{3}(\mathbf{a} + \mathbf{b} + \mathbf{c})$, so both triangles have G as their centroid.

   (c) By the Euler line property for triangle XYZ, $\mathbf{HK} = 3\mathbf{HG}$, so K has position vector $-\mathbf{a} - \mathbf{b} - \mathbf{c}$. It follows that O is the midpoint of HK.

4. The point of concurrence is T, the centre of the Nine-Point Circle. In fact T is the midpoint of each of AU, BV and CW. To prove this you will require $\mathbf{OU} = 2\mathbf{OL} = (\mathbf{b} + \mathbf{c})$.

5. Let $\mathbf{a_1}$ be the position vector of A_1 etc. Then

$$\mathbf{p_1} = \mathbf{a_2} + \mathbf{a_3}, \mathbf{q_4} = \mathbf{a_1} + \mathbf{a_2} + \mathbf{a_3}, \mathbf{x} = \mathbf{a_1} + \mathbf{a_2} + \mathbf{a_3} + \mathbf{a_4}.$$

6. Each of the triangles has the same circumcentre, the centre of the circle in which $ABCD$ is inscribed. So take this to be the origin of vectors. Let A have position vector $\mathbf{a}$ etc. For part (c) the orthocentre H_1 of triangle BCD is at

$\mathbf{h_1} = \mathbf{b} + \mathbf{c} + \mathbf{d}$ and the orthocentre H_2 of triangle ACD is at $\mathbf{h_2} = \mathbf{a} + \mathbf{c} + \mathbf{d}$. Then $\mathbf{H_2H_1} = \mathbf{h_1} - \mathbf{h_2} = \mathbf{b} - \mathbf{a} = \mathbf{AB}$. Similarly the other sides of $H_1 H_2 H_3 H_4$ are equal and parallel to the sides of $ABCD$ and hence the congruence. Parts (a) and (b) produce similarities rather than congruences because of the factors $\frac{1}{3}$ and $\frac{1}{2}$ in the vector positions of the centroid and nine-point centre respectively, otherwise the working is identical.

7.3 Unit 15: The use of rectangular Cartesian co-ordinates

First we give a list of formulae that are commonly encountered and which the reader should regard as exercises to be completed or as results to be learned from other sources if not already met before. In all that follows $P_1(x_1, y_1)$, $P_2(x_2, y_2)$, $P_3(x_3, y_3)$, are arbitrary points. Unless otherwise stated they are distinct and non-collinear. O is the origin of co-ordinates $(0,0)$.

(1) The midpoint of $P_1 P_2$ has co-ordinates $(\frac{1}{2}(x_1+x_2), \frac{1}{2}(y_1+y_2))$.

(2) $(P_1 P_2)^2 = (x_2 - x_1)^2 + (y_2 - y_1)^2$.

(3) A straight line not parallel to the y-axis may be expressed in the form $y = mx + c$, where m is the **slope** or **gradient** of the line, and c is the $y-$**intercept** (the value of y when $x = 0$). A straight line parallel to the y-axis is of the form $x = d$, where d is the perpendicular distance from the y-axis. However all lines may be expressed in the form $ux + vy = w$, and this avoids having to consider as a special case any line parallel to the y-axis.

(4) Two lines with equations $y = m_1 x + c_1$, $y = m_2 x + c_2$ $(m_1, m_2 \neq 0)$ are perpendicular to each other if and only if $m_1 m_2 = -1$. Added to this is the singular case that all lines of the form $y = c$ are perpendicular to all lines of the form $x = d$. Two lines with equations $u_1 x + v_1 y = w_1$ and $u_2 x + v_2 y = w_2$ are perpendicular if and only if $u_1 u_2 + v_1 v_2 = 0$, and again the use of equations in this form does away with the need to consider special cases. For example, the lines with equations $2x + 3y = 7$ and $3x - 2y = 4$ are perpendicular. Note the useful technique of "exchanging the coefficients

of x and y and changing the sign of one of them" to obtain a perpendicular line.

(5) The point of intersection of two lines, if it exists, is found by solving the equations of the lines as a simultaneous pair. Thus the two lines in (4) have a point of intersection with co-ordinates $(2, 1)$.

(6) The area of triangle OP_1P_2 is given by

$$
\begin{aligned}
[OP_1P_2] &= \tfrac{1}{2}(x_1y_2 - x_2y_1) \\
&= \tfrac{1}{2}\det\begin{pmatrix} x_1 & y_1 \\ x_2 & y_2 \end{pmatrix}
\end{aligned}
$$

where the lettering of the vertices of the triangle in an anti-clockwise order is OP_1P_2.

(7) More generally, the area of triangle $P_1P_2P_3$ is given by

$$
[P_1P_2P_3] = \frac{1}{2}\det\begin{pmatrix} 1 & 1 & 1 \\ x_1 & x_2 & x_3 \\ y_1 & y_2 & y_3 \end{pmatrix},
$$

where the lettering of the vertices of the triangle in an anti-clockwise order is $P_1P_2P_3$.

(8) The equation of the line P_1P_2 is

$$
(x_2 - x_1)y - (y_2 - y_1)x = (x_2y_1 - x_1y_2).
$$

(9) (i) The perpendicular distance from O on to the line with equation

$$
ux + vy = w
$$

is given by

$$
|w|/(u^2 + v^2)^{\frac{1}{2}}.
$$

(ii) The perpendicular distance from P_3 to the same line is given by

$$\frac{|w - ux_3 - vy_3|}{\sqrt{u^2 + v^2}}.$$

(iii) The perpendicular distance of P_3 from the line $P_1 P_2$ is

$$\frac{1}{\sqrt{(x_2 - x_1)^2 + (y_2 - y_1)^2}} \det \begin{pmatrix} 1 & 1 & 1 \\ x_1 & x_2 & x_3 \\ y_1 & y_2 & y_3 \end{pmatrix}$$

as is most easily obtained from (2) and (7).

(iv) The perpendicular distance between the parallel lines with equations

$$ux + vy = w_1 \quad \text{and} \quad ux + vy = w_2$$

is

$$\frac{1}{\sqrt{u^2 + v^2}} |w_1 - w_2|.$$

(10)   (i) The angle s between the line with equation $y = mx + c$ and the x-axis is given by $\tan s = m$.

(ii) The angle t between the lines with equations $y = m_1 x + c_1$ and $y = m_2 x + c_2$ is given by

$$\tan t = (m_2 - m_1)/(1 + m_1 m_2), \quad (m_1 m_2 \neq -1),$$

and is 90° when $m_1 m_2 = -1$.

(iii) The angle t between the lines with equations

$$u_1 x + v_1 y = w_1 \quad \text{and} \quad u_2 x + v_2 y = w_2$$

is given by

$$\cos t = \frac{\sqrt{u_1 u_2 + v_1 v_2}}{\sqrt{u_1^2 + v_2^2} \sqrt{u_2^2 + v_2^2}}.$$

(iv) The angle t between the vectors $\mathbf{OP_1}$ and $\mathbf{OP_2}$ is given by
$$\cos t = \frac{x_1 x_2 + y_1 y_2}{\sqrt{x_1^2 + y_1^2}\sqrt{x_2^2 + y_2^2}}.$$

(11) (i) P_3 lies on the line $P_1 P_2$ if and only if
$$x_1 y_2 + x_2 y_3 + x_3 y_1 = x_1 y_3 + x_2 y_1 + x_3 y_2.$$

(ii) P_3 lies on $P_1 P_2$ if and only if real numbers c and d exist with $c + d = 1$ such that $x_3 = cx_1 + dx_2$ and $y_3 = cy_1 + dy_2$.

(12) (i) The equation of the circle centre P_1, radius r is given by
$$(x - x_1)^2 + (y - y_1)^2 = r^2.$$

(ii) The circle with equation
$$x^2 + y^2 + 2gx + 2fy + c = 0, \ c < g^2 + f^2,$$
has centre $C(-g, -f)$ and radius $r = (g^2 + f^2 - c)^{\frac{1}{2}}$.

(iii) The equation of the circle on $P_1 P_2$ as diameter is
$$(x - x_1)(x - x_2) + (y - y_1)(y - y_2) = 0.$$

(13) (i) The equation of the tangent at $P(a, b)$ to the circle with equation as given in (12)(ii) is
$$ax + by + g(x + a) + f(y + b) + c = 0,$$
where $a^2 + b^2 + 2ga + 2fb + c = 0$.

(ii) In particular the equation of the tangent at $P(r \cos t, r \sin t)$ to the circle centre O and radius r is
$$x \cos t + y \sin t = r.$$

(14) (i) The power of the point $P(a, b)$ with respect to the circle S with equation as given in (12)(ii) is

$$a^2 + b^2 + 2ga + 2fb + c.$$

This is equal to $PC^2 - r^2$, where C is the centre of S and r its radius. If P is external to the circle this is the square of the length of the tangent from P to S. P lies outside, inside or on S according as the above expression is $>, <,$ or $= 0$) respectively.

(ii) In particular the power of the point P with respect to the circle S_0 with equation $x^2 + y^2 = r^2$ is $a^2 + b^2 - r^2$.

(15) There are two particularly useful parameterizations of points on the circle S_0. These are:

(i) $x = r \cos t, y = r \sin t, (0 \le t < 2\pi$ or $-\pi < t \le \pi)$;

(ii) $x = r\{(1 - t^2)/(1 + t^2)\}, y = r\{(2t)/(1 + t^2)\}$, $(-\infty < t < \infty)$.

Corresponding equations of tangents at 't' are:

(i) $x \cos t + y \sin t = r$;

(ii) $x(1 - t^2) + 2yt = r(1 + t^2)$.

Chords joining 's' and 't' have equations:

(i) $x \cos \frac{1}{2}(s + t) + y \sin \frac{1}{2}(s + t) = r \cos \frac{1}{2}(s - t)$;

(ii) $x(1 - st) + y(s + t) = r(1 + st)$.

The simplicity of the second parameterization makes it particularly useful in application to problems involving chords and tangents

(16) The condition for circles S_1 and S_2 with equations

$$S_1 \quad : \quad x^2 + y^2 + 2g_1 x + 2f_1 y + c_1 = 0,$$
$$S_2 \quad : \quad x^2 + y^2 + 2g_2 x + 2f_2 y + c_2 = 0,$$

to cut orthogonally is that the distance between their centres is equal to $(r_1^2 + r_2^2)^{\frac{1}{2}}$, where r_1, r_2 are their respective radii. This condition simplifies to

$$2(g_1 g_2 + f_1 f_2) = (c_1 + c_2).$$

(17) Points P_1 and P_2 are said to be **conjugate** points with respect to the circle S_0 if and only if

$$P_1 P_2^2 = OP_1^2 + OP_2^2 - 2r^2.$$

This condition simplifies to

$$x_1 x_2 + y_1 y_2 = r^2.$$

In the more general case with the circle S the condition simplifies to

$$x_1 x_2 + y_1 y_2 + g(x_1 + x_2) + f(y_1 + y_2) + c = 0.$$

When $OP_1 P_2$ is a straight line the condition becomes

$$(OP_1)(OP_2) = r^2$$

and P_1 and P_2 are said to be **inverse** points.

(18) Taking the **polar** of the point P_1 to be the locus of its conjugate points we obtain for the polar of P_1 with respect to S_0 the straight line with equation

$$x_1 x + y_1 y = r^2,$$

and with respect to S the straight line with equation

$$x_1 x + y_1 y + g(x + x_1) + f(y + y_1) + c = 0.$$

Observe that these become the equations of tangents when P_1 lies on the circle. When P_1 lies outside the circle the polar is the straight line joining the points of contact of the tangent P_1 to the circle whose polars pass through P_1.

(19) The equation of the radical axis of the circles S_1, S_2 given in (16) is the locus of points P such that the powers of P with respect to S_1 and S_2 are equal. This condition simplifies to

$$2(g_1 - g_2)x + 2(f_1 - f_2)y + (c_1 - c_2) = 0.$$

It is perpendicular to the line of centres which has gradient $(f_1 - f_2)/(g_1 - g_2)$.

(20) (i) The system of circles with equations

$$x^2 + y^2 + 2gx + c = 0,$$

for varying g and **fixed** c possess a common radical axis $x = 0$ and their centres all lie on the line $y = 0$. Such a system is said to form a **coaxal system**.

(ii) If $c < 0$ each circle of the system passes through the two fixed points $(0, \sqrt{-c}), (0, -\sqrt{-c})$ and we have an **intersecting system of coaxal circles**.

(iii) If $c = 0$ each circle touches the radical axis $x = 0$ and we have a **touching system of coaxal circles**.

(iv) If $c > 0$ the value of g must be restricted to the range $|g| > \sqrt{c}$ and the limiting cases $g = \sqrt{c}, -\sqrt{c}$ correspond to circles of zero radius, that is the point circles as the **limiting points** $(\sqrt{c}, 0), (-\sqrt{c}, 0)$ and we have a **non-intersecting system of coaxal circles**.

(v) Inspection of the orthogonality condition in (16) shows that every member of the above coaxal system is orthogonal to every member of the complementary coaxal system in which the circles have equations

$$x^2 + y^2 + 2fy - c = 0,$$

with varying f and the **same fixed value of** c. This second system share a radical axis which is the line of centres of the first system and vice versa. The change of sign of c means that the complementary system of coaxal circles is of the opposite type to the original system in the case of intersecting and non-intersecting systems, and of the same type for touching systems.

We now give some worked examples to illustrate various techniques used in co-ordinate geometry for solving problems. These and the set of exercises that follow illustrate the sort of problems that are suitable for solution by the co-ordinate methods outlined in this Unit.

Worked Examples

1. Find the condition on u, v, w for the line with equation $ux + vy = w$ to touch the circle with equation $x^2 + y^2 = r^2$.

Method 1: Double Roots
The idea is that a line meets a circle in two points, whose co-ordinates are determined from their equations. The two points result from the roots of a quadratic equation. When the roots are real and distinct the line intersects the circle in a chord, when the two roots are equal the line is a tangent, and when they are complex the line does not intersect the circle at all. Following

this procedure, eliminating the variable y we obtain the quadratic equation

$$(u^2 + v^2)x^2 - 2uwx + (w^2 - r^2v^2) = 0.$$

The condition for equal roots is $u^2w^2 = (u^2+v^2)(w^2-r^2v^2)$, leading to $v = 0$ or $|w| = r(u^2 + v^2)^{\frac{1}{2}}$. When $v = 0, x = w/u$ and $y^2 = r^2 - w^2/u^2$. The two values of y from this are equal if and only if $y = 0$, leading to $|w| = ur$. This case is subsumed by the alternative, so the required condition is covered by the single equation $|w| = r(u^2 + y^2)^{\frac{1}{2}}$.

Method 2 : Comparison of Coefficients

We know all tangents to the circle with equation $x^2 + y^2 = r^2$ are of the form $x \cos t + y \sin t = r$. If $ux + vy = w$ is one of these then $u : v : w = \cos t : \sin t : r$. Hence $r^2(u^2 + v^2) = w^2$, so the required condition is $|w| = r(u^2 + v^2)^{\frac{1}{2}}$.

Method 3: Use of a known Geometrical Fact

In this case the known fact is that the perpendicular distance from the centre of a circle on to a tangent is equal to its radius. Using formula (9)(i) this leads immediately to the equation

$$r = |w|/(u^2 + v^2)^{\frac{1}{2}},$$

the required condition once again.

2. From the external point $P_0(x_0, y_0)$ tangents are drawn to the circle with equation $x^2 + y^2 = r^2$. Find the equation of the chord joining the points of contact.

Method 1: Symmetric Functions of Roots of Equations

It is not efficient in this type of question to write down the equation of an arbitrary line through P_0 and put in the condition that it is a tangent, but instead it is better to write down the equation of a tangent and put in the condition that it passes through P_0. It may seem at first to be a minor matter to adopt one approach rather than the other, but in fact it is things of this kind that differentiate between success and failure. From (15) the tangent at 'u' to $x^2 + y^2 = r^2$ is

$$x(1 - u^2) + 2yu = r(1 + u^2).$$

If this passes through $P_0(x_0, y_0)$ then we get the quadratic equation

$$(r + x_0)u^2 - 2y_0u + (r - x_0) = 0,$$

indicating that there are two tangents passing through P_0. If $u = s, t$ are the roots of this equation then, again from (15), the equation of the required chord is

$$x(1 - st) + y(s + t) = r(1 + st).$$

The fact that only the symmetric functions $(s + t)$ and st occur in this equation, as is inevitable by virtue of symmetry, means that we do not need to solve the quadratic equation, but instead we may use the theory of roots of equations to give

$$(s + t) = 2y_0/(r + x_0) \text{ and } st = (r - x_0)/(r + x_0).$$

This means that $(1 - st) : (s + t) : (1 + st) = x_0 : y_0 : r$. Hence the equation of the chord of contact is

$$x_0x + y_0y = r^2.$$

Method 2 : Use of a known Geometrical Fact

The known fact is that the chord of contact is the polar of P_0, and from (18) this is

$$x_0x + y_0y = r^2.$$

The brevity of Method 2 hides the fact that the equation of the polar has to be derived by some means, and if not by Method 1, then by some method very similar to it.

3. A variable circle cuts a fixed circle orthogonally and passes through a fixed point; prove that the locus of its centre is a straight line.

Method 1 : Sensible choice of Origin and Axes

There is no loss of generality in choosing the origin of co-ordinates and the direction of the axes to make the working in the solution of a problem as straightforward as possible. In addition it is possible to choose one distance in the problem to be equal to one unit, but this has the disadvantage that one may lose track of the dimension of an expression and hence not notice a mistake. In this particular problem it is sensible to choose the centre of the fixed circle as origin, and to put the fixed point on the x-axis at say $(d, 0)$. Let the radius of this circle be r, then its equation is $x^2 + y^2 = r^2$. Flexibility of choice has now been used up so we have to choose for the variable circle the general equation $x^2 + y^2 + 2gx + 2fy + c = 0$. From (16) the condition for orthogonality of the two circles is $c = r^2$. The condition that the circle passes through $(d, 0)$ is $d^2 + 2gd + c = 0$. It follows that $g = -\frac{1}{2}(d + r^2/d)$ and f may have any value. The locus of the centre $(-g, -f)$ of the variable circle is therefore the line with equation $x = \frac{1}{2}(d + \frac{r^2}{d})$.

Method 2 : Use of a known Geometrical Fact

The locus is the radical axis of the coaxal system defined by the fixed circle and the fixed point as a limiting point.

In addition to illustrating some of the important techniques that are often used in co-ordinate geometry the above examples also show how factual knowledge of pure geometrical results may reduce the amount of work needed, and it is certainly true that pure geometrical methods are often shorter and more elegant that co-ordinate methods. However, as a fourth example, we establish Poncelet's porism using co-ordinate geometry. A **porism**, whether in algebra or geometry, is a problem that has no solution unless some particular condition is satisfied, but when that condition is satisfied it has an infinity of solutions. An example is that a quadrilateral with sides a, b, c, d (in that order) has no inscribed circle unless $a + c = b + d$, but when this condition is satisfied then **all** quadrilaterals with these side lengths possess an inscribed circle.

4. **Poncelet's Porism**

If C_O is a circle, centre O and radius R, and C_I is a circle, centre I and radius r, $r \leq \frac{1}{2}R$, lying entirely within C_O, then there is no triangle ABC that can be simultaneously inscribed in C_O and circumscribed to C_I unless $IO^2 = R^2 - 2Rr$. But when this equation is satisfied there are an infinity of such triangles.

O is the obvious origin of co-ordinates and OI may be chosen as the x-axis, with I having co-ordinates $(d, 0)$, where $d^2 = R^2 - 2Rr$. With these choices C_O has equation $x^2 + y^2 = R^2$ and C_I has equation $(x - d)^2 + y^2 = r^2$. The method of solution is to show that starting with **any** point T on C_O then after drawing tangents TU, TV to C_I, then UV is a tangent to C_I as well. In this way each triangle TUV qualifies as a suitable triangle.

First from (15), the equation of a chord TW of C_O joining parameters 't' and 'w' is

$$x(1 - tw) + y(t + w) = R(1 + tw).$$

Now put in the condition that the perpendicular distance from $I(d, 0)$ on to this line is r, providing the condition that TW is a tangent to C_I. This gives, on squaring,

$$(R - d)^2 + 2(R^2 - d^2)tw + (R + d)^2 t^2 w^2 = r^2(1 + t^2)(1 + w^2). \quad (*)$$

For fixed t, this is a quadratic in w, the roots of which, u and v, give the positions U and V respectively on C_O. We wish to show that UV is a tangent to C_I, and this involves showing equation(*) holds with t, w replaced by u, v. In order to ease the algebra, put $R+d = l, R-d = m$, so that $l+m = 2R$ and $lm = R^2 - d^2 = 2Rr$. It follows that $lm/(l+m) = r$ or $1/r = 1/l + 1/m$. Now put $l/r = h$ and $m/r = k$ then $h + k = hk$. Furthermore in terms of h, k equation (*) becomes

$$k^2 + 2hktw + h^2t^2w^2 = (1+t^2)(1+w^2),$$

or rearranged as a quadratic in w

$$w^2\{t^2(h^2 - 1) - 1\} + 2hktw + \{(k^2 - 1) - t^2\} = 0.$$

It follows that

$$u+v = 2hkt/\{(1-t^2(h^2-1))\}, uv = \{(k^2-1)-t^2\}/\{t^2(h^2-1)-1\}.$$

From here on it is only a question of algebraic manipulation to show that, given $h + k = hk$, the equation

$$k^2 + 2hkuv + h^2u^2v^2 - (1+u^2)(1+v^2)$$

holds.

Exercises

1. Let $ABCD$ be a cyclic quadrilateral, with A, C fixed and B, D variable on arcs AC, CA respectively, so that $BC = CD$. Let M be the point of intersection of AC and BD. Find the locus of the circumcentre of triangle AMB.

2. Let ABC be a triangle with angle $A = 90°$. Let X be the foot of the perpendicular from A to BC and Y the midpoint of XC. Let AB be extended to D so that $AB = BD$. Prove that DX is perpendicular to AY.

3. The diameter AB of a circle is extended to C so that $BC = AB$; the tangent at A and a line parallel to it through C are drawn and any point P being taken on the latter the two tangents from P are drawn forming a triangle with the tangent at A. Prove that as P varies this triangle has a fixed centroid.

4. AB is a diameter of a circle and a chord through A meets the tangent at B at a point P. On the extension of AP a point Q is chosen and QR, QS are the tangents from Q to the circle. The extensions of AR, AS meet the tangent at B in X, Y respectively. Prove that $PX = PY$.

5. A tangent is drawn at a fixed point A on a circle. P is a variable point on a line parallel to the tangent, on the other side of it from the circle. The tangents from P to the circle meet the tangent at A at Q and R. Prove that $(QA)(AR)$ is constant.

7.4 Unit 16: Hints and Solutions

1. Take C to be $(1,0)$ and the circle to have radius 1. If A has co-ordinates $(\cos t, \sin t)$ then the locus of the circumcentre of triangle AMB is a circle, centre $(-\frac{1}{2}, \frac{1}{2}\cot\frac{1}{2}t)$, radius $\frac{1}{2}\csc\frac{1}{2}t$. It passes through the origin O.

2. Take A to be the origin and $B(k,0), C(0,h)$. Then show X has co-ordinates

$$(\frac{h^2 k}{h^2 + k^2}, \frac{hk^2}{h^2 + k^2}).$$

D is $(2k,0)$. Now it is straightforward to show that the gradient of AY is $(h^2 + 2k^2)/hk$ and that of XD is $-hk/(h^2 + 2k^2)$.

3. Take $A(-1,0)$ and $B(1,0)$ so that $C(3,0)$. The tangent to the circle at parameter 't' has equation

$$x(1 - t^2) + 2ty = (1 + t^2).$$

This passes through the variable point $P(3,k)$, where k is a parameter, provided $2t^2 - tk - 1 = 0$, showing there are two such tangents with $t = u, v$ where $u + v = \frac{k}{2}$ and $uv = -\frac{1}{2}$. Now the two tangents meet the line $x = -1$ at the point $(-1, \frac{1}{u})$ and $(-1, \frac{1}{v})$. The midpoint Y of these two points is now easily calculated as $(-1, -\frac{1}{2}k)$ and the line PY meets the line ABC at the **fixed** point $G(\frac{1}{3},0)$ which is such that $AG : GB = 2 : 1$.

4. Take $A(-1,0)$ and $B(1,0)$. Let the chord through A have equation $y = m(x + 1)$ so that P has co-ordinates $(1, 2m)$ and suppose Q has co-ordinates $(k, m(k + 1))$, where k is a parameter. The tangent at 't' has equation

$$(1 - t^2)x + 2ty = (1 + t^2)$$

and the condition that this passes through Q is $t^2(1 + k) - 2tm(1+k) + (1-k) = 0$, showing there are two such tangents with $t = u, v$ where $u+v = 2m$ and $uv = (1-k)/(1+k)$. It is now straightforward to show that X and Y have co-ordinates $(1, 2u)$ and $(1, 2v)$ respectively. The midpoint of XY is thus $(1, u + v) = (1, 2m)$, which is the point P.

5. Take the circle to be of unit radius, centre the origin, and $A(1,0)$. Suppose the perpendicular distance between the two parallel lines is d, and take P to have co-ordinates $(1 + d, k)$, where k is a parameter. The tangent at 't' has equation $(1 - t^2)x + 2ty = 1 + t^2$ and the condition that it passes through P is $t^2(2 + d) - 2tk - d = 0$. This shows there are two such tangents with $t = u, v$ where

$$u + v = \frac{2k}{2 + d} \text{ and } uv = \frac{-d}{(d + 2)}.$$

The tangents meet $x = 1$ at $(1, \frac{1}{u})$ and $(1, \frac{1}{v})$ and hence $(QA)(AR) = \frac{1}{|uv|} = \frac{d}{(d+2)}$, a constant independent of k.

7.5   Unit 17: The use of complex numbers

Key Formulae

The following notation is used. The point A in the two-dimensional Euclidean plane is associated with the complex number a in the Argand diagram. The co-ordinates of the point A correspond to the real and imaginary parts of a, and these are denoted by x_A, y_A respectively. Thus $a = x_A + iy_A$. A brief review of key formulae is now given.

(1) $a + b = (x_A + x_B) + i(y_A + y_B)$.

(2) $a - b = (x_A - x_B) + i(y_A - y_B)$.

(3) $ab = (x_A x_B - y_A y_B) + i(x_A y_B + x_B y_A)$.

(4) $a^* = (x_A - iy_A)$, the **complex conjugate** of a, associated with the reflection of A in the x-axis.

(5) $\frac{1}{2}(ab^* + a^*b) = x_A x_B + y_A y_B = \mathbf{OA.OB}$, defining (a, b), the scalar product of two complex numbers.

(6) $(ab^* + a^*b)/2i = x_A y_B - y_A x_B = \mathbf{OA} \times \mathbf{OB}$, defining $a \times b$, the exterior product of two complex numbers.

(7) $(a, a) = aa^* = |a|^2 = x_A^2 + y_A^2 = OA^2$. $|a|$ is called the **modulus** of a. It represents the distance of A from the origin.

(8) From (1) and (7) we have

$$|a - b| = \{(x_A - x_B)^2 + (y_A - y_B)^2\}^{\frac{1}{2}} = BA.$$

Also the displacement $\mathbf{BA}$ in the Euclidean plane is placed in correspondence with the line segment $(a - b)$ in the Argand diagram.

(9) If $a = |a|(\cos t_A + i \sin t_A) = |a| \exp(it_A)(-\pi < t_A \leq \pi)$, then t_A is called the **principal argument** of a. One often reads $\arg a = t_A$, with the '(mod 2π)' understood. t_A is the angle OA makes with positive direction of the x-axis. Note that the points on the negative x-axis have argument equal to π.

(10) $|ab| = |a||b|$ and $\arg(ab) = t_A + t_B$.

(11) $1/a = a^*/(aa^*) = a^*/(|a|^2), a \neq 0$. This property enables one to divide by a complex number making the denominator of a fraction real.

(12) $|a/b| = |a|/|b|$ and $\arg(a/b) = \arg a - \arg b$. In particular $|1/a| = 1/|a|$ and $\arg(1/a) = -\arg a$.

(13) $\arg(a - b)$ represents the angle directed line segment BA makes with the positive direction of the x-axis.

(14) **de Moivre's theorem**:

$$(\cos t_A + i \sin t_A)^n = \cos(nt_A) + i \sin(nt_A),$$

for all integral n. If n is a rational this formula provides one of the many values a rational power of a complex number may take. For example if $n = \frac{1}{3}$ then there are three possible cube roots, namely

$$\cos(\frac{1}{3}(t_A + 2k\pi)) + i \sin(\frac{1}{3}(t_A + 2k\pi))$$

for $k = 0, 1, 2$. In fact the formula may be modified to deal with powers of an irrational or complex number, provided care is taken over arguments. Some functions become infinite-valued, for example, using the form in (9), one finds $\log a = \log |a| + it_A$, where any multiple of 2π may be added to or subtracted from t_A.

It may seem, because complex numbers provide a synthesis between co-ordinates and vectors, that they ought to provide the ultimate tool for handling planar geometrical problems. That this is not the case seems to be because the equations of lines and circles using complex numbers are rather complicated by comparison, this being associated with the unwieldy form of the complex number scalar product. The use of complex numbers has an advantage in one important situation. It lies in the fact that if $c = a \exp(it)$, then since $|c| = |a|$ and $\arg c = \arg a + t$ (directed angles being used here). There is no such compact way of managing such a rotation using co-ordinates or vectors. Further properties that may be of use are now given, with the letter z being used as a variable point or current co-ordinate.

(15) **The triangle inequality**: $|a - b| \leq |a| + |b|$ and $|a + b| \leq |a| + |b|$.

(16) The point P dividing AB in the ratio $l : m$ is associated with the complex number p given by $p = (ma + lb)/(l + m)$.

(17) The equation of the line AB is $z(b^* - a^*) - z^*(b - a) = ab^* - a^*b$. Note that in terms of the exterior product of the complex numbers this may be written as $z \times b + b \times a + a \times z = 0$.

(18) The area of triangle OAB is $\frac{1}{2}(a \times b)$, with the usual convention for sign, and more generally, the area of triangle ABC is $\frac{1}{2}(a \times b + b \times c + c \times a)$.

(19) In terms of the scalar product the equation of a line may be expressed in the form $(z, u) = d$ where d is a real number, and this line is perpendicular to the direction of OU, and the perpendicular distance from O on to this line is $|d|/|u|$.

(20) The angle t between the lines OA and OB is given by $\cos t = (a, b)/(|a||b|)$.

(21) The circle, centre C and radius r has equation $|z - c| = r$. Without the modulus notation this takes on the rather ugly form $zz^* - c^*z - cz^* + cc^* - r^2 = 0$.

(22) The circle on AB as diameter has equation $(z - a, z - b) = 0$.

(23) If A lies on the circle, centre C and radius r, then the equation of the tangent at A is given by $(z - c, a - c) = r^2$. If A does not lie on the circle this is the equation of the polar of A.

(24) Sometimes it is useful to parameterize the circle $|z| = r$ by writing $z = r\exp(it)$, with r fixed and $-\pi < t \leq \pi$.

(25) The condition for the two circles, centres C_1, C_2 given by

$$zz^* - c_1^*z - c_1z^* + k_1 = 0 \quad \text{and} \quad zz^* - c_2^*z - c_2z^* + k_2 = 0$$

to cut orthogonally is $2(c_1, c_2) = k_1 + k_2$.

(26) The equation of the perpendicular bisector of the line AB is

$$z(a^* - b^*) + z^*(a - b) = aa^* - bb^*.$$

(27) The half line AP, excluding A, making an angle t with the positive direction of the x-axis may be written in the form $\arg(z - a) = t$.

(28) If A and B are two fixed points then the locus of the point P such that $\angle APB = t(\mod \pi)$, is a circle through A and B (but excluding them) and it may be written in the form $\arg(z - b) - \arg(z - a) = t(\mod \pi)$, where t is fixed and lies in the interval $0 < t < \pi$.

Exercises

1. Let A and B be the points associated with $a = -1$ and $b = 1$. Prove that the locus of a point P such that $AP = k \times BP$ (where $k \neq 1$) is a circle, and find its centre and radius. (This circle is called the circle of Apollonius.)

2. With A and B as in Exercise 1 and D represented by $d = \frac{1}{3}(5 + 4i)$, prove that the internal bisector of $\angle ABD$ makes an angle of 45° with AB.

3. If the perpendicular from A to BC meets the circumcircle, centre the origin, again at D_1 prove that $d_1 = -bc/a$. Hence show that D, the foot of the perpendicular from A to BC has position d, relative to O, given by $d = (a^2 + ab - bc + ca)/(2a)$.

4. If T is the Nine-Point Centre represented by $t = \frac{1}{2}(a + b + c)$, prove that $TD = TE = TF = \frac{1}{2}R$, where D, E, F are the feet of the altitudes from A, B, C respectively.

Worked Example 1 Show that A, B, C are the vertices of an equilateral triangle if and only if the complex numbers representing their positions satisfy the equation

$$a^2 + b^2 + c^2 - bc - ca - ab = 0.$$

Since a, b, c are unequal the given equation implies $(a - b)/(c - b) = (b - c)/(a - c)$, and this is equivalent to $AB/BC = BC/CA$ **and** $\angle B = \angle C$, these being the modulus and argument forms of the previous equation. This again is equivalent to $(AB)(CA) = (BC)^2$ and $CA = AB$, which in turn implies $AB = BC = CA$. This argument is reversible, so the condition stated is both necessary and sufficient.

Exercise

5. Equilateral triangles are erected externally on the sides of an arbitrary triangle ABC. Prove that the centroids of these three equilateral triangles themselves form an equilateral triangle.

Worked Example 2 $ABCD$ is a parallelogram. On its sides squares are constructed outwards so that they lie external to the parallelogram. Let M_1, M_2, M_3, M_4 be their centres. Prove that $M_1M_2M_3M_4$ is a square.

Take the origin to be the intersection of AC and BD, then $c = -a$ and $d = -b$. Let E be the midpoint of AB, then $e = \frac{1}{2}(a + b)$. Now $EM_1 = EB$ and $\angle BEM_1 = 90^\circ$ (using directed angles). It follows that $m_1 = e + i(b - e) = \frac{1}{2}\{a(1 - i) + b(1 + i)\}$. Similarly $m_2 = \frac{1}{2}\{b(1 - i) + c(1 + i)\} = \frac{1}{2}\{-a(1 + i) + b(1 - i)\}$. Likewise $m_3 = \frac{1}{2}\{c(1 - i) + d(1 + i)\} = -\frac{1}{2}\{a(1 - i) + b(1 + i)\}$ and $m_4 = \frac{1}{2}\{d(1 - i) + a(1 + i)\} = \frac{1}{2}\{a(1 + i) - b(1 - i)\}$. Now the line segment M_1M_2 is represented by $(m_2 - m_1) = -a - ib$. Also $(m_3 - m_2) = ia - b = -i(m_2 - m_1)$. Thus $M_1M_2 = M_2M_3$ and $\angle M_1M_2M_3 = 90^\circ$. Similarly for other sides.

Exercises

6. On the sides of an arbitrary convex quadrilateral $ABCD$ squares are constructed, all lying external to the quadrilateral, with centres L, M, N, P (in that order round the quadrilateral). Show that $LN = NP$.

7. On the sides of an arbitrary convex quadrilateral $ABCD$, equilateral triangles are constructed, alternately inwards and outwards. Prove that their vertices, other than A, B, C, D form a parallelogram.

8. $ABCD$ is a convex quadrilateral with squares drawn outwards on the four sides. These squares have centres L, M, N, P forming a second quadrilateral. Prove that the midpoints of AC, BD, LN, MP form a square.

7.6 Unit 17: Hints and Solutions

1. Using z for the variable point P, we obtain the equation $|z+1| = k|z-1|$. Now put $z = x + iy$ and square. We then obtain the Cartesian equation of a circle, centre C and radius r, where $c = (k^2+1)/(k^2-1)$ and $r = (c^2-1)^{\frac{1}{2}} = 2|k|/|k^2-1|$.

2. Put $k = 2$ in the result for Exercise 1. The centre of the circle is at $c = \frac{5}{3}$, and its radius is $\frac{4}{3}$. This means that D lies on the circle and $DA = 2DB$. The points P_1 and P_2, given by $\frac{1}{3}$ and 3 respectively, lie on AB and provide a diameter of the circle. The internal bisector of $\angle ADB$ divides AB internally in the ratio $2 : 1$ and so meets AB at P_1 Now $\angle P_1 D P_2 = 90^o$ (angle in a semi-circle). But $DP_1 = DP_2$ since CD is at right angles to AB. Hence $\angle DP_1 P_2 = 45^o$.

3. Take BC parallel to the real axis, without loss of generality, and $a = R\exp(is)$, $b = R\exp(it)$, $c = R\exp(iu)$ and $d_1 = R\exp(iv)$. Let K be the midpoint of AD_1, then $\arg k = 0$. Let L be the midpoint of BC, then $\arg l = \frac{1}{2}(t+u)$. But OK and OL are at right angles so $\arg l = -\pi/2$. It follows that $bc = R^2\exp(i(t+u)) = (-iR)^2 = -R^2$ and hence $-bc/a = R\exp(-is)$. But $v = -s$ and hence $d_1 = -bc/a$. For the second part use $HD = DD_1$ and $h = a + b + c$.

4. Use the results of Exercise 3. You should find the displacement from T to D, given by $|d-t| = |d_1| = \frac{1}{2}R$ and similarly for TE and TF.

5. This result is attributed to Napoleon. To answer this question you need to find the complex number representing the point A_1 on the opposite side of BC to A such that A_1BC is an equilateral triangle. Justify $a_1 = b - w(c - b)$, where $w = \exp(2\pi i/3)$. Note that $w^3 = 1, 1 + w + w^2 = 0$ and $w^* = w^2$.

It follows that $a_1 = -w^2b - wc$. The centroid of triangle A_1BC is therefore represented by the complex number

$$a_G = \frac{1}{3}(b(1 - w^2) + c(1 - w)).$$

The centroids b_G, c_G of triangles B_1CA, C_1AB respectively follow by cyclic change. It now remains to verify that

$$a_G^2 + b_G^2 + c_G^2 - b_Gc_G - c_Ga_G - a_Gb_G = 0.$$

(See Worked Example 1.)

6. Let L be the centre of the square erected on AB. Then $l = \frac{1}{2}\{(a + b) + i(b - a)\}$ and in the same way

$$n = \frac{1}{2}\{(c + d) + i(d - c)\}.$$

The displacement $\mathbf{LN}$ is therefore represented by

$$\frac{1}{2}\{(c + d - a - b) + i(d - c - b + a)\}.$$

Likewise the displacement $\mathbf{MP}$ is represented by

$$\frac{1}{2}\{(d + a - b - c) + i(a - d - c + b)\}.$$

It is now clear that $(n - l) = i(p - m)$, so not only is $LN = MP$, but also they are at right angles.

7. Take $ABCD$ to be a clockwise lettering and suppose the triangles ALB and CND are external, and BMC and DPA internal. Then

$$l - b + w(b - a), \quad m = c + w^*(c - b),$$

$$n = d + w(d - c) \text{ and } p = a + w^*(a - d),$$

where $w = \exp(2\pi i/3)$. It follows that $(m - l) = (n - p) = w(a - c)$. This means that LM and NP are equal in length and parallel, so $LMNP$ is a parallelogram.

8. Use the results from Exercise 6, that $l = \frac{1}{2}\{(a+b)+i(b-a)\}$, with m, n, p given by cyclic change of a, b, c, d. The midpoint U of LN is therefore given by $u = \frac{1}{4}\{(a+b+c+d)+i(b-a+d-c)\}$. The midpoint V of MP is given by $v = \frac{1}{4}\{(a+b+c+d)+i(c-b+a-d)\}$. The midpoint S of AC is given by $s = \frac{1}{2}(a+c)$ and the midpoint T of BD is given by $t = \frac{1}{2}(b+d)$. Now $(v-u) = (i/2)(a+c-b-d)$ and $(s-t) = \frac{1}{2}(a+c-b-d)$, proving the result.

7.7   Unit 18: Inversion

Definition and Introduction

The **inverse** of a point Z with respect to a circle S_A, centre A and radius r, is defined to be the point W on AZ (or its extension) such that $(AZ)(AW) = r^2$, it being understood that Z and W are on the same side of A as each other. In terms of the complex numbers a, z, w representing A, Z, W respectively, this becomes

$$(w - a)(z^* - a^*) = r^2.$$

The modulus of this equation gives $(AZ)(AW) = r^2$ and its argument ensures that A, Z, W lie on a line through A with both Z and W on the same side of A as each other.

If A is the origin this takes on the simpler form $wz^* = r^2$, and in what follows, in dealing with the theory of the topic, it is convenient to take the **circle of inversion**, as it is called, to have centre the origin. If A is the centre it is called the **centre of inversion**.

If one thinks of all points in the z-plane undergoing the transformation of inversion, $wz^* = w|z|^2/z = r^2$, that is $w = zr^2/|z|^2$, their images all lie in the w-plane, and so a geometrical figure in the z-plane transforms into another geometrical figure in the w-plane, called the **inverse figure**. A problem concerning the original figure thereby has its counterpoint in connection with the inverse figure. The use of inversion in solving problems is to transform the problem into one that is easier to solve. Skill in applying the method is first to recognize those problems that are suitable for treatment by inversion and secondly to choose the centre of inversion in such a way that the transformed problem becomes straightforward. Note that a change in the value of r does nothing except alter the value of w by a constant real multiplicative factor. Different values of

r lead to similar figures. For this reason a phrase such as "invert with respect to the point A" is often used, specifying the centre of inversion, but not bothering to specify the radius of the circle of inversion.

An important point to realize is that the centre of inversion in the z-plane is mapped on to the point at infinity in the w-plane and vice versa. Sometimes the original figure and the inverted figure are drawn as separate diagrams, but in other cases it is helpful to superimpose the w-plane on the z-plane. In any case it is always well to remember that $|z| < r$ transforms into $|w| > r$ and $|z| > r$ transforms into $|w| < r$.

Theorem 1

(a) If a straight line is inverted with respect to a point O on the line, the inverse is a straight line through O, having the same orientation;

(b) If a circle is inverted with respect to a point O on the circle, the inverse is a straight line perpendicular to the diameter through O;

(c) If a straight line is inverted with respect to a point O not on the straight line, the inverse is a circle through O with centre on the perpendicular from O on to the line;

(d) If a circle is inverted with respect to a point O not on the circle the inverse is a circle and O lies on the line of centres of the two circles.

Proof

Let the line or circle in the z-plane have equation

$$bzz^* - c^*z - cz^* + k = 0, \qquad (*)$$

where c is some complex number and b, k are real number. In Cartesian co-ordinates, with $c = -g - if$, where g, f are real this becomes

$$b(x^2 + y^2) + 2gx + 2fy + k = 0.$$

The four cases in the theorem correspond respectively to:

(a) $b = 0, k = 0$ and the straight line has equation $gx + fy = 0$;

(b) $b = 1, k = 0$ and the equation of the circle is

$$x^2 + y^2 + 2gx + 2fy = 0,$$

with centre $(-g, -f)$ and radius $\sqrt{g^2 + f^2}$.

(c) $b = 0$ and $k = 2h$, say, and the line has equation

$$gx + fy + h = 0;$$

(d) $b = 1$ and the circle has equation

$$x^2 + y^2 + 2gx + 2fy + k = 0,$$

with centre $(-g, -f)$ and radius $\sqrt{g^2 + f^2 - k}$.

For simplicity take $r = 1$ and then with O the centre of inversion the transformation takes the form $wz^* = 1$, so that $z = 1/w^*$. The image of $(*)$ under this inversion is

$$kww^* - c^*w - cw^* + b = 0.$$

With u, v as real co-ordinates in the w-plane this becomes

$$k(u^2 + v^2) + 2gu + 2fv + b = 0.$$

The four cases in the theorem now correspond to:

(a) $b = 0, k = 0$. So the image is the straight line with equation $gu + fv = 0$, having the same gradient in the w-plane as the original line in the z-plane;

(b) $b = 1, k = 0$. So the image is the straight line with equation $2gu + 2fv + 1 = 0$, a line perpendicular to the diameter through O of the original circle. In fact the line has gradient $-g/f$ and the diameter has gradient f/g;

(c) $b = 0, k = 2h$. So the image is the circle with equation $h(u^2 + v^2) + gu + fv = 0$, and this circle passes through the origin in the w-plane and has centre $(-g/2h, -f/2h)$. The equation of the perpendicular from O to the original line has equation $gy = fx$, and this contains the centre of the circle;

(d) $b = 1$. So the image is the circle with equation

$$k(u^2 + v^2) + 2gu + 2fv + 1 = 0,$$

and with centre $(-g/k, -f/k)$ and radius $\sqrt{g^2 + f^2 - k}/k$. The centre and radius of the original circle have forms that are equal to k times these quantities, and hence O lies on the line of centres of the two circles. It is important to note that the centres of the two circles are **not** corresponding points of the inversion. ∎

The transformation of inversion is an involution; that is, if it is applied twice one gets back to the original figure in the z-plane, or in other words the composition of two applications is the identity transformation.

To summarize the situation when the inverse figure is superimposed on the original figure:

A straight line through O maps on to itself, but a point close to O in the z-plane, with $|z| < 1$, has an image far away in the w-plane, with $|w| > 1$ and vice versa.

A circle S_A, centre A, passing through O maps on to a straight line perpendicular to OA. And a line not through O maps on to a circle, the centre A of which is such that OA is perpendicular to the line.

A circle not through O maps on to a second circle and O lies in that line.

Theorem 2

At the corresponding points of intersection, the angle at which two curves intersect is equal to the angle at which the inverse curves intersect.

Proof

Let C_1, C_2 be the curves meeting at Z, with Z_1, Z_2 close to Z on C_1, C_2 respectively. Let W, W_1, W_2 be the corresponding inverse points. Then

$$(w - w_1)/(w - w_2) = (z^* - z_1^*)/(z^* - z_2^*) \times (z_2^*/z_1^*).$$

It follows that

$$\arg(w - w_1) - \arg(w - w_2) = \arg z_1 - \arg z_2 + \arg(z - z_2) - \arg(z - z_1).$$

In the limit as Z_1, Z_2 tend to Z, $\arg z_1$ tends to $\arg z_2$ and the left hand side becomes the angle between the images of C_1, C_2 and the right hand side becomes the angle between C_1, C_2. These angles are actually directed in the opposite sense, but that is seldom significant. ∎

Theorem 2 is significant and in particular provides the following results:

(i) A pair of orthogonal circles in general, inverts into a pair of orthogonal circles.

(ii) If a pair of orthogonal circles meet at O, the centre of inversion, their inverses are a pair of straight lines at right angles to each other.

(iii) If a pair of orthogonal circles are such that one passes through O, the centre of inversion, and the other does not pass through O, then their inverses are a circle and a diameter to that circle.

(iv) If two curves touch, then their inverse curves touch, or if the inverses are lines then those lines are parallel.

Exercises

1. (i) What is the inverse of a circle with respect to its centre?

    (ii) What is the inverse of a pair of parallel lines?

    (iii) What is the inverse of an intersecting coaxal system of circles with respect to one of the points of intersection?

    (iv) What is the inverse of a non-intersecting system of coaxal circles with respect to one of its limiting points?

2. In general, how many circles can be drawn through a given point to touch two non-intersecting circles?

3. Suppose that P and Q lie on the same arc AB of a circle. It follows that $\angle APB = \angle AQB$. What does this theorem become on inversion with respect to A?

Worked Example
The Simson line property is that if P is a point on the circle ABC and L, M, N are the feet of the perpendiculars from P on to the chords BC, CA, AB respectively, then L, M, N are collinear. What result is obtained by inverting with respect to P?

In what follows the inverse of X is denoted by X^*. The circle $PABC$ inverts into the line $A^*B^*C^*$. The chord BC inverts into the circle PB^*C^*. The line PL inverts into the line PL^* and since PL is perpendicular to BC, the line PL^* becomes a diameter of the circle PB^*C^* and for this to be so L^* must be at the opposite end of the diameter to P. Likewise PM^* is a diameter of circle PC^*A^* and

PN^* is a diameter of circle PA^*B^*. The conclusion that LMN is a straight line becomes the property that P, L^*, M^*, N^* are concyclic. The circle homothetic to circle $PL^*M^*N^*$ and half the radius and centre of similitude P evidently passes through the circumcentres of triangles $PB^*C^*, PC^*A^*, PA^*B^*$. So the inverse of the Simson line property with respect to P is that if A^*, B^*, C^*, lie on a line and P is not a point on that line, then the circumcentres of triangles $PB^*C^*, PC^*A^*, PA^*B^*$ are concyclic with P.

Exercises

4. Invert with respect to H the result that the altitudes of a triangle are concurrent at H.

5. O, A, B, C, H are five points such that circles OAB, OCH are orthogonal, and circles OBC, OAH are orthogonal. Prove that circles OCA, OBH are also orthogonal.

6. P is a fixed point, l is a fixed line. Q, R are variable points on l such that $\angle QPR = $ constant. Prove that the circumcircle of triangle PQR touches a fixed circle.

7. Two circles intersect at O and B. Let ABC be a chord through B terminated by points A, C lying one on each circle. Prove that the angle the two circles cut plus $\angle COA = 180^o$.

8. Invert the following theorem with respect to C:
   Parallel lines l, m, n contain the non-collinear points A, B, C respectively. n lies between l and m. AB is perpendicular to l, m, n. The circle on AB as diameter meets n at D, a point distinct from C. Circles ADC, BDC meet l, m at E, F respectively. Then l and m are both tangents to circle ECF.

Thus far the properties of inversion we have been concerned with are those involving incidence including the values of the angles at which lines and circles meet. There is a further class of problems, in which distances are involved, that are capable of analysis by inversion and some in which the precise value of r, the radius of the circle of inversion needs to be chosen. Sometimes such problems require the inverted figure to be superimposed on the original figure, thereby providing a duality of meaning. In order to proceed we require a theorem relating distances in the original and inverted figures.

Theorem 3
If O is the common origin in the z-plane and the w-plane, and Z_1, W_1 and Z_2, W_2 are corresponding pairs of points related by the inversion $wz^* = r^2$, then

$$W_1 W_2 / Z_1 Z_2 = r^2 / \{(OZ_1)(OZ_2)\} = \{(OW_1)(OW_2)\}/r^2.$$

Proof
We have $w_1 = r^2/z_1^*$ and $w_2 = r^2/z_2^*$, so

$$\frac{W_1 W_2}{Z_1 Z_2} = \frac{|w_1 - w_2|}{|z_1 - z_2|} = r^2 \frac{|1/z_1^* - 1/z_2^*|}{|z_1 - z_2|} = \frac{r^2}{|z_1||z_2|} = \frac{r^2}{(OZ_1)(OZ_2)}.$$

The second part of the theorem follows immediately from this, since

$$(OW_1)(OW_2)(OZ_1)(OZ_2) = r^4.$$

Worked Example: Ptolemy's theorem and its extension
Prove that if A, B, C, D are any four points in a plane, then

$$(AB)(CD) + (BC)(DA) \geq (AC)(BD),$$

with equality if and only if $ABCD$ is a cyclic quadrilateral (with the order of vertices being A, B, C, D either clockwise or anti-clockwise).

Invert with respect to A, then B, C, D become the three points B^*, C^*, D^* for which the triangle inequality holds, namely

$$B^*C^* + C^*D^* \geq B^*D^*,$$

with equality if and only if B^*, C^*, D^* is a straight line with C^* an internal point of B^*D^*. It follows from Theorem 3 that

$$\frac{(BC)}{(AB)(AC)} + \frac{(CD)}{(AC)(AD)} \geq \frac{(BD)}{(AB)(AD)}.$$

Clearing fractions provides the required inequality. Moreover B^*, C^*, D^* is a straight line if and only if a circle BCD passes through A, and C^* is an internal point of B^*D^* if and only if the ordering of the vertices around the cyclic quadrilateral is A, B, C, D.

Exercises

9. What is the inverse of Ceva's theorem with respect to the point of concurrence?

10. If $OAMC$, $OBCL$, $OANB$ are circles meeting at O (with points in the order stated) prove O, L, M, N are concyclic if and only if

$$\{(BL)(CM)(AN)\}/\{(LC)(MA)(NB)\} = 1.$$

11. $P_0, P_1, P_2, \ldots, P_n$ are $(n+1)$ points on a circle (with points in the order stated). Prove that

$$P_1P_2/\{(P_0P_1)(P_0P_2)\} + P_2P_3/\{(P_0P_2)(P_0P_3)\} + \ldots + \\ + \ldots + P_{n-1}P_n\{(P_0P_{n-1})(P_0P_n)\} = P_1P_n/\{(P_0P_1)(P_0P_n)\}.$$

12. Invert a parallelogram $ABCD$ with respect to A and state the theorems corresponding to the fact that the diagonals AC and BD bisect each other at a point P.

13. A, B, C are three collinear points. O is a point such that $\angle AOB = \angle BOC$. By inverting with respect to O, prove that $OA/OC = AB/BC$.

14. S is the inverse of P with respect to a circle. QSR is any chord. Prove that PS bisects $\angle QPR$.

7.8 Unit 18: Hints and Solutions

1. (i) Either itself or a concentric circle.

   (ii) Either circles touching at the centre of inversion, or a circle and its tangent at the centre of inversion (the latter being the case if the centre of inversion lies on one of the lines).

   (iii) A system of concurrent lines meeting at the inverse of the other point of intersection.

   (iv) A system of concentric circles with centre the inverse of the other limiting point.

2. Four, one corresponding to each of the four common tangents.

3. Let the inverse of B be B^*. The circle becomes a line l through B^*, but not passing through A. Let the inverse of P be P^*. Then for any point P^* on l, the line AP^* meets the circle AP^*B^* (the inverse of the line PB) at a constant angle. That is to say the angle between AP^* and the tangent P^* is constant. Since this constant angle is the angle AB^* makes with l, it is evident that the theorem is essentially the alternate segment theorem.

4. If three circles $B^*HC^*, C^*HA^*, A^*HB^*$ are such that the centres of circles B^*HC^*, C^*HA^* lie on A^*H, B^*H respectively, then the centre of circle A^*HB^* lies on C^*H.

5. Invert with respect to O. Note that a pair of orthogonal circles inverts into a pair of perpendicular lines. The theorem now follows as a consequence of the altitudes of a triangle being concurrent.

6. Invert with respect to P. l becomes a fixed circle through P. Q^* and R^*, the inverses of Q and R respectively are variable

points on the circle. $\angle QPR = \angle Q^*PR^*$ remains constant. All such chords Q^*R^* are of fixed length and they are all tangents to a concentric circle. In the original figure Q^*R^* corresponds to the circumcircle PQR. Since Q^*R^* touches a fixed circle, it follows that the circumcircle PQR touches a fixed circle also, the inverse of which is the concentric circle above.

7. Invert with respect to O. The line ABC becomes the circle $A^*B^*C^*O$. The circle OAB becomes the line A^*B^* and the circle OBC becomes the line B^*C^*. Angles are perserved so the angle between the circles is the same as $\angle A^*B^*C^*$ and the $\angle AOC$ is the same as $\angle A^*OC^*$. But $\angle A^*B^*C^* + \angle A^*OC^* = 180^o$, since $A^*B^*C^*O$ is a cyclic quadrilateral.

8. Using the symbol $*$ to denote the inverse of an entity, then l^*, m^* are circles touching externally at C, with common tangent n^*. The circle ABD touches at l and m, so its inverse is a circle $A^*B^*D^*$ touching l^* and m^*, and meeting n^* at D^*. The circle ADC has inverse the line A^*D^* and this meets l^* at E^*. Likewise the inverse of the circle BDC is the line D^*B^* which meets m^* at F^*. The theorem is that E^*F^* is tangent to both l^* and m^*. Note that there are two possible positions of D^*, and the second position leads to the other common tangent of l^* and m^*.

9. Circles LBC, MCA, NAB meet at P. If APL, BPM, CPN are straight lines then

$$\frac{(BL)(CM)(AN)}{(LC)(MA)(NB)} = 1.$$

10. Invert with respect to O and the result follows from Menelaus's theorem

Index